EVERYTHING YOU EVER WANTED TO KNOW ABOUT TEXAS

BY KIRK DOOLEY

HALF COURT PRESS

Published by
HALF COURT PRESS
16475 Dallas Parkway
Suite 650
Dallas, TX 75248

Copyright© 1986 by Kirk Dooley

All rights reserved. No part of this book may be reproduced in any form or by any means without the prior written permission of the Publisher, excepting brief quotes used in connection with reviews, written specifically for inclusion in a magazine or newspaper or broadcast.

Manufactured in the United States
by Hicks Printing, Garland, Texas

Cover Design by John March.

To Miss Charlotte

who still hasn't quite figured out
what she's gotten herself into....

"You go to hell. I'm going to Texas!"

—*Davy Crockett*

Acknowledgments

Encouragement and support from family and friends have made this project possible. Jim Moroney III deserves as much blame for this book as I. He is my longtime friend, teammate, traveling companion, drinking buddy, business partner, Maryville Marauder, raccoon fisherman and co-conspirator of numerous semi-civilized festivities. His faith in my eclectic ideas has always delighted and inspired me.

John Carpenter III and Bond Beams have hung in there with their prodigal "little brother" over the years. Rick "Racehorse" Addison's victory on my behalf at the *Battle of Park Cities People* ranks him up there with Sam Houston himself. Pete Bibby, Jere Thompson, Jr., Buster Haas, Phillip Wiggins, Kellis White and Rayburn Myers are appreciated for their encouragement over the years.

When the Texas Trivia board game was being researched, the following Texas experts contributed: Russ Pate, Pete Oppel, Eben Price, Philip Wuntch and Dr. June Welch of Dallas; Scott Kelm (who should be writing sports right now) and Daryl "Dr. Trivia" Andersen of Houston. A big "Phi Alpha" to my favorite designer, John March, who has been with me for years and just keeps getting better.

Muchas Gracias to Les South, the king of Hicks Printing. He and Charlotte Whitesides, Lynda Prather, Cindy Damer, Mike Duke, Robin Walden, Ron Regan, Jean Hardin, John Karlovich and the rest of my teammates at Hicks have gone beyond the call of duty.

Others who have lent their support along the way include Art Barnes, Dr. Bill Dean, Fred Hill, David Witts, Jere and Peggy Thompson, Gary Wood, Steve Ramsey, Bob Arnold, Buddy and Kaki Hayden, Kim Palmer, Bert Shipp, Angie Enright, Janyce Brannon, Clarita Robertson, Danny P. Little, Larry and Betty Arnspiger, Sammy Papert, Bragg Smith, Bill and Barbara Hitzelberger (and their Bird-dog), Jim and Lynn Moroney and their family (which is almost my family, too). Special *Boomer Sooner* thanks to Bob and Bette Beams.

My sister Molly has served as my personal nurse and enchilada cook while my TERRIFIC brother, Patrick O. Dooley, keeps me motivated and inspired. My brother Craig (who is my business partner) and our chief administrator at Dooley Homes, Kathy Blackwell, have allowed me the spare time to compile this book of Texana.

Finally, to my shellshocked but hearty Irish-Texan parents, Clyde and Dorothy Dooley, thanks for all the years of support, encouragement, direction and understanding.

—K.D.

Everything You Ever Wanted to Know About Texas

By Kirk Dooley

1 What Dallas-area native won the 1986 NBA Slam Dunk contest at Reunion Arena?

A Ira Terrell
B "Too Tall" Jones
C Martina Navratilova
D Spud Webb

2 What was the name of George Jones first hit single?

A "He Stopped Loving Her Today"
B "Why Baby Why"
C D-I-V-O-R-C-E
D "I Was Country When Country Wasn't Cool"

3 Who was killed in a plane crash with Wiley Post?

A Buddy Holly
B Amelia Earhart
C C.W. Post
D Will Rogers

4 Where is Lowenbrau brewed in Texas?

A Fort Worth
B San Antonio
C Shiner
D Schulenberg

5 Where is Texas' "fly-in" bank?"?

A Love Field
B Terlingua
C Rio Vista
D Bankledesh

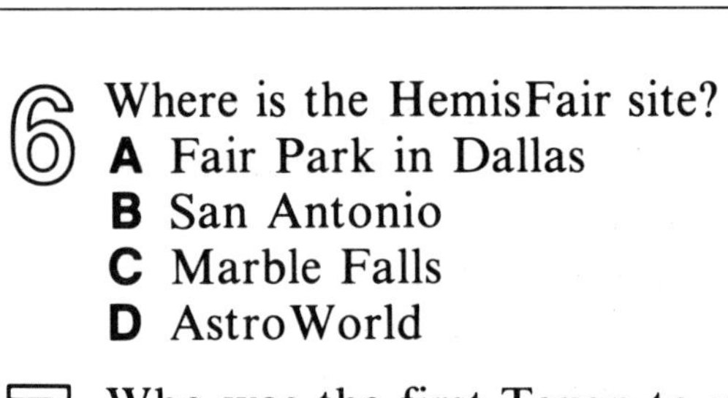

6 Where is the HemisFair site?

A Fair Park in Dallas
B San Antonio
C Marble Falls
D AstroWorld

7 Who was the first Texan to walk on the moon?

A Billie Sol Estes
B John Glenn
C Alan Bean
D George Jetson

8 In the bumper sticker, "I'm Mad Too, Eddie," who's Eddie?

A Eddie Albert
B Eddie Chiles
C Ed Haggar
D Eddie Rabbit

9 Who's daughter played the woman who shot J.R.?

A Bing Crosby
B Joe Bob Principal
C Mary Martin
D Mary Ann Smith

10 What Texan wrote and directed the movie, "Places in the Heart"?

A Horton Foote
B William Wittliff
C Sally Field
D Robert Benton

11 Name the first football field to use artificial turf.

A Texas Stadium
B Kyle Field
C Astrodome
D Plano High School

12 Which Amtrak route runs through Alpine, Texas?

A *The Chilihead Zephyr*
B *The Sunset Limited*
C *The Cannonball Express*
D *The Greydog Redeye Special*

13 Where was Dr Pepper invented?

A College Station
B Waco
C Dallas
D El Paso

14 Where did Stephen F. Austin locate his first Texas colonists in 1823?

A The Mansion on Turtle Creek
B San Felipe
C Washington-on-the-Brazos
D Lakeway

15 How many counties are there in the Great State of Texas?

A 54
B 154
C 254
D 354

16 What town is noted as the town "where the West begins"?

A El Paso
B Beaumont
C Texarkana
D Ft. Worth

17 Where did the Sesquicentennial Wagon Train start in January, 1986?

A Sulphur Springs
B Hot Springs
C Dripping Springs
D Rock Springs

18 What stadium has been known as "the House that Doak Built"?

A Ownby Stadium at SMU
B Doak Walker Sports Center
C The Cotton Bowl
D Texas Stadium

19 Why is the statue atop the Texas Capitol Building facing South?

A Anti-Union sentiments were strong when it was constructed
B Better view of the Colorado River
C A Blue Norther can't freeze the statue
D The Texas Constitution outlawed statues facing east

Where did Morgan Fairchild go to college?

A Rice
B Trinity
C Texas Tech
D SMU

Whose band was called the "Texas Playboys"?

A Hugh Bob Hefner
B Lance Rentzel
C Bob Wills
D Ernest Tubb

Where is Miss Black-Eyed Pea crowned?

A Athens, Texas
B Paris, Texas
C London, Texas
D Moscow, Texas

23 What is the state tree of Texas?

A Redwood
B Hackberry
C Palm
D Pecan

Who quarterbacked Navy in Navy's loss to Texas in the 1964 Cotton Bowl?

A General Archie Westmoreland
B Roger Staubach
C Kenny Stabler
D Gary Hogeboom

25 Fill in the blank: Billy _____ _____ Johnson.

A Bob Lyndon
B White Shoes
C Joe Bob
D Boom Boom

26 Corsicana was the first Texas town to have what:

A 7-Eleven
B Bennigan's
C Gas lights
D Legalized chicken ranching

27 Who was the Texas Rangers' first 20-gamer winner?

A Randy Galloway
B Nobody
C Ferguson Jenkins
D Brad Corbett

28 Name the first Texas college to play football in Europe (versus Henderson State of Arkansas in 1976).

A Texas A&I
B Texas Southern
C Texas A&M
D Texas Tech

29 What breed of dog is the Texas A&M mascot?

A Walrus
B Collie
C Doberman pincher
D Poodle

30 What actress became famous playing Sue Ellen on "Dallas"?

A Victoria Principal
B Lori Palmer
C Sissy Spacek
D Linda Gray

31 Who is Elmore Torn?

A Inventor of the margarita
B Heir apparent to Henry Cisneros in San Antonio
C Rip Torn
D Amarillo oil tycoon who tried to take over Gulf Oil

32 Who sang, "Dang Me"?

A Paul Thayer
B Roger Miller
C Frank Zappa
D Governor Bill Clements

33 Who wrote "Terms of Endearment"?

A James Michener
B A.C. Greene
C Joe Bob Briggs
D Larry McMurtry

34 Who did not die on February 3, 1959?

A The Big Bopper
B Patsy Cline
C Buddy Holly
D Richie Valens

35 Where are Texas' largest sand dunnes?
A Dumas
B Sandhill State Park at Monahans
C Lufkin
D Six Flags Over Texas

36 The first rodeo ever held took place in what West Texas town in 1883?
A Longview
B Midland
C Pecos
D Graham

37 Where is baseball's longest dugout?
A Astrodome
B Arlington Stadium
C Disch-Falk Field in Austin
D Arc Park in Fort Worth

38 Where is the Sun Bowl held each December?
A Wichita Falls
B El Paso
C Houston
D Juarez

39 What Texas band had a hit song called "D.O.A."?
A Bloodrock
B Coconuts
C Joe "King" Carrasco and the Crowns
D The Crickets

40 Which of the following is Carlton Stowers' book about high school football in Texas?

A *Friday Night Heroes*
B *Making the Mo$t of Recruiting*
C *Saturday Morning Has-Beens*
D *Meat on the Hoof*

Where was Larry Gatlin raised?

A Scagway, Alaska
B Austin, Texas
C Hollywood, California
D Odessa, Texas

In terms of income, what is usually Texas' most profitable industry?

A Tourism
B Football recruiting
C Petroleum
D High Tech

43 What university was organized in 1845 by the Baptists, in Independence, Texas?

A Texas Christian University
B Baylor
C Wayland Baptist
D Rice

44 What park in Texas contains 703,221 acres?

A Big Bend National Park
B Town Lake in Austin
C Garner State Park
D Highland Park

Name the fourth flag to fly over Texas.
A Mexico
B Confederacy
C Republic of Texas
D France

Sam Houston's son, Andrew Jackson Houston, was appointed as interim Texas senator in 1941, at the age of 87. How long did he serve before he died?
A Twenty minutes
B Six years
C Three weeks
D He is still serving

When is San Jacinto Day?
A March 2
B April 21
C Everyday
D Cinco de Mayo

Which Texas city has the most historical markers?
A Houston
B El Paso
C San Antonio
D Austin

Name the first air-conditioned hotel in Texas.
A St. Anthony's in San Antonio
B Adophus in Dallas
C Texas in Ft. Worth
D Motel NoTell in LaGrange

50 Name the largest football stadium in regular SWC play.
A Texas Tech's Jones Stadium
B Texas Stadium (SMU)
C UT-Austin's Memorial Stadium
D Texas A&M's Kyle Field

51 What former TCU star receiver was traded by the Houston Oilers to the Dallas Cowboys in return for Butch Johnson?
A Jack Spikes
B Bob Lilly
C Mike Renfro
D Billy "White Shoes" Johnson

52 Name two movies in which Debra Winger played young Texas housewives.
A "An Officer and a Gentleman"
B "Terms of Endearment"
C "Debra Does Omaha"
D "Urban Cowboy"

53 Who played the son of Rock Hudson and Elizabeth Taylor in "Giant"?
A Dennis Hopper
B James Dean
C Ron Howard
D Kareem Olajuwon

54 What is Dasypus novemcinctus?
A Latin for "Wishbone offense"
B Armadillo

C Marvin Zindler's real name
D A chili cookoff antacid, handed out free

55 What NFL coach is from Mission, Texas?
A Mike Ditka
B Dan Reeves
C Tom Landry
D Don Shula

56 Where was the Texas Declaration of Independence signed?
A Joe Miller's
B Washington-on-the-Brazos
C Austin
D The Alamo

57 What role did Gene Wilder play in the movie "Bonnie and Clyde"?
A Eugene, the undertaker
B Clyde Barrow
C The mad scientist
D Texas Ranger Frank Hamer

58 WBAP-AM in Fort Worth was the first radio station to broadcast a country music show. What was the name of it?
A Louisiana Hayride
B Barn Dance
C All-Night Country Road Show
D Hee-Haw

To which Dallas hospital was President Kennedy rushed, after his shooting?

A Parkland
B Methodist
C Medical City
D Baylor

Name the oldest university in Denton.

A North Texas State University
B Texas Woman's University
C Rice
D Denton High

How long did the Battle of Jan Jacinto last?

A 18 minutes
B 13 days
C Two weeks
D It's still being fought

In a Lubbock cemetary there is a guitar-shaped gravestone belonging to whom?

A Buddy Holly
B John Belushi
C Jim Reeves
D Patsy Cline

63 Where are Texas' most treasured Botanic Gardens (built during the depression)?

A Marfa
B Bug Tussle
C Fort Worth
D Duval County

What is the significance of Bush Mountain?
A A Beer is brewed there
B Tallest mountain in Texas
C Home mountain of Vice President George Bush
D Second tallest peak in Texas

The town of Nocona, Texas, was named for:
A A brand of cowboy boots
B A Pontiac
C Chief Peta Nocona
D The feared nocona snake

Which present day large Texas city was once a temporary capital of the Republic of Texas?
A Houston
B Dallas
C San Antonio
D Muleshoe

Who was the Dallas Cowboy's middle linebacker before Lee Roy Jordan?
A Bob Breunig
B Eugene Lockhart
C Chuck Howley
D Jerry Tubbs

Who was the first SWC soccer All-American?
A Greg Ryan of SMU
B Kyle Rote, Jr. of the University of the South

C Tom Schutz of Texas Tech
D Iseed Khoury of North Texas State

Name Jayne Mansfield's only hit movie.
A "You Can't Take it With You"
B "The Girl Can't Help It"
C "Debbie Does Dallas"
D "Gentlemen Prefer Blondes"

70 Where is all the gold in California, according to Larry Gatlin?
A Marin County
B Yosemite
C Bank of America
D In a bank in the middle of Beverly Hills, in somebody else's name

71 What is the most popular lake in Texas, as far as visitors go?
A Lake Texhoma
B Lake Conroe
C Lake Travis
D Lake Ransom Canyon

72 What is long and sandy and sits between Laguna Madre and the Gulf of Mexico?
A Texas
B Padre Island
C The ghost of Good Fellowship Rare
D $200,000,000,000 worth of sand dollars

Which one of the following is not a cousin to the others?

A Mickey Gilley
B Jerry Lee Lewis
C Jimmy Swaggart
D Earl Campbell

74 What Texas beauty was James Bond's catch in "Moonraker"?
A Farrah Fawcett
B Nancy Lieberman
C Lois Chiles
D Candy Barr

75 Name the third busiest airport in Texas.
A Temple International
B Hobby Airport
C D/FW International
D Houston Intercontinental

76 Why did 61,000 Houstonians crowd into the Astrodome on November 22, 1965?
A To hear the Beatles
B To see the Astros beat the Mets
C To attend Billy Graham's rally
D Rice was picked to beat Texas by three

77 What did the Texas Legislature vote to do on February 1, 1861?
A Attack Mexico
B Install orange light on the UT Tower

C Seceed from the Union and join the Confederacy
D Outlaw barbed wire

78 Albert Latimer was the youngest Texan to
A Win the Heisman Trophy
B Graduate from Texas A&M
C Die at the Battle of the Alamo
D Sign the Texas Declaration of Independence

79 How many men were said to have been killed by John Wesley Hardin by the time he turned 21?
A None
B One
C At least 21
D 148

80 Whose attire infuriated prosecutors in the Jack Ruby murder trail?
A Lee Harvey Oswald
B Jack Ruby
C District Attorney Henry Wade
D Ruby's attorney Melvin Belli

81 Who was Ross Perot Jr.'s co-pilot when they became the first pilots to circumnavigate the world in a helicopter?
A God
B Bull Simmons
C Jay Coburn
D Sky King

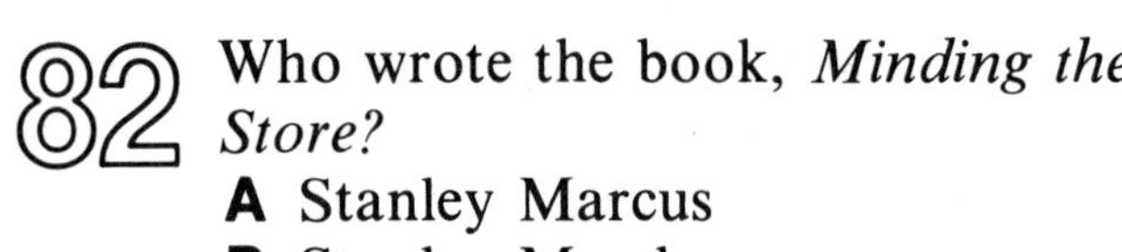

82 Who wrote the book, *Minding the Store?*

A Stanley Marcus
B Stanley Marsh
C Robert Sakowitz
D Joe Bob Briggs

83 Who won an Oscar for his acting in the Texas-filmed movie, "Tender Mercies"?

A Robert Duvall
B Jerry Haynes
C John Knight
D Gary Busey

84 This town used to be called Waterloo.

A Muleshoe
B Earth
C Cut 'N Shoot
D Austin

85 Where is the world's largest rattlesnake roundup held?

A West Uganda
B Houston
C Sweetwater
D Buffalo Gap

86 Where do Jeff and Hazel live?

A Mount Vernon
B Sante Fe
C San Antonio
D San Marcos

87 Who released an album called "Stardust"?

A Janis Joplin
B The Big Bopper
C Freddy Fender
D Willie Nelson

88 What actor made a name for himself playing the role of Ray Krebs in the TV show, "Dallas"?

A Patrick Duffy
B Larry Hagman
C Steve Kanaly
D Ken Kerchival

89 Who wrote the novel, *Celebrity?*

A Dan Jenkins
B Blackie Sherrod
C Bud Shrake
D Thomas Thompson

90 Name Jerry Jeff Walker's back-up band during his Viva Terlingua days.

A The Ace in the Hole Band
B The Lost Gonzo Band
C The Texas Troubadors
D Gerry and the Pacemakers

91 Who directed the movie, "The Alamo"?

A John Wayne
B Chill Wills
C Richard Widmark
D Santa Anna

92 Identify Houston's "Big E."
A Elvis' nickname in Houston
B Earl Campbell's CB handle
C Elvin Hayes (former Houston Cougar basketball star)
D The Energy industry

93 What former SMU star led the NFL in scoring in 1950 and 1955?
A Sean Stopperich
B Art Barnes
C Doak Walker
D Kyle Rote

94 What was the name of the Houston band which did the "Tighten Up"?
A Archie Bell and the Drells
B Buck Owens and Buckaroos
C Buddy Holly and the Cricketts
D Gladys Knight and the Pips

95 Lake Meredith, in the Texas panhandle, is fed by what river?
A Red River
B Brazos River
C Mississippi River
D Canadian River

96 What beer is brewed in the "Country of 1100 Springs"?
A Lone Star
B Shiner
C Falstaff
D Pearl

97 What is the state gem?
A Topaz
B Emerald
C Ruby
D George Gervin

98 Marvin Lee Aday goes by what single name?
A Liberace
B Meatloaf
C Prince
D Marvin

99 What member of the Charles Manson "family" is from Texas?
A Icky Twerp
B Marvin Zindler
C Bill Macatee
D Tex Watson

100 Name the stadium where Texas' only Super Bowl was held.
A Texas Stadium
B Rice Stadium
C Astrodome
D Cotton Bowl

101 Who wrote the play *Vanities?*
A Beth Henley
B Don Coburn
C Preston Jones
D Jack Heifner

102 What did "GTT" mean across the USA in the 1800's?

A General Telephone and Telegraph
B GTT was the original version of the GTO
C "Gone to Texas"
D "Go Texas Tech!"

103 What was the name of the building from which the shots were fired that killed President Kennedy?
A Dealey Plaza
B Dallas County Courthouse
C Texas Schoolbook Depository
D Hertz Rent-A-Car Building

104 Which town on the Guadalupe River was named for a Prussian prince?
A New Braunfels
B Tahoka
C Refugio
D Study Butte

105 What 1962 movie about a state fair was shot in Dallas?
A "Bonnie and Clyde"
B "State Fair"
C "Halford's Mountain"
D "Carny"

106 What hurricane hit Brownsville in 1967?
A Beulah
B Modell
C Stell
D Nell

107 Seymour, Texas, holds the record for the _____ _____ in Texas.

A Smartest cows
B Hottest day
C Prettiest women truck drivers
D Tallest skyscraper

108 Which college is not in Abilene:

A Hardin Simmons
B Abilene Christian
C McMurray
D Stephen F. Austin

109 What Dallas Cowboy was "the world's fastest human"?

A Jethro Pugh
B Eddie LeBaron
C Bob Hayes
D Doug Donley

110 Name the two men who were awarded the first two American Football League franchises.

A Bud Adams of Houston
B T. Boone Pickens of Amarillo
C Neal Gay of Mesquite
D Lamar Hunt of Dallas

111 Name the movie for which Dorothy Malone won her Oscar.

A "Written on the Wind"
B "Animal House"
C "Breakfast at Tiffany's"
D "Peyton Place"

112 Who had the hit song, "96 Tears"?
- **A** Jay and the Americans
- **B** Joe "King" Carrasco and the Crowns
- **C** ? and the Mysterians
- **D** Herman's Hermits

113 What event in 1901 completely changed the state's economy?
- **A** The Texas-OU games was initiated at the Cotton Bowl
- **B** H.L. Hunt was born
- **C** Will Rogers met a man he didn't like
- **D** Oil was discovered

114 Which election box became famous in Lyndon Johnson's 1948 senatorial race?
- **A** Box 13, Jim Wells County
- **B** Box 23, Nueces County
- **C** The South Box, Potter County
- **D** Cloyce Box, Collin County

115 Why was artificial turf originally placed in the Astrodome?
- **A** It was cheaper than real grass
- **B** It was greener than real grass
- **C** Real grass wouldn't grow in the Astrodome
- **D** Artificial turf doesn't have to be mowed as much

116 What did Candy Mongtomery use to kill her friend, Betty Gore, in the highly-publicized Wylie, Texas,

murder?
A A weedeater
B An ax
C The butler
D A seven iron

117 Name the greatest Texas Kiowa chief, or at least make a guess.
A Santanta (or White Bear)
B Sonny Sixkiller
C Tonto (or Kimosabe)
D Running Dear

118 Who was the West Texas wheeler-dealer convicted in a large fertilizer scam?
A Billy Bob Harris
B Billy Gibbons
C Billie Sol Estes
D Billy Joe Dupree

119 What major office did Price Daniel, Jr. hold in the Texas legislature?
A Speaker of the House
B Governor
C Lt. Governor
D Mark White's pilot

120 What Ft. Worth actress played Grizabella in "Cats" on Broadway?
A Katherine Stewart
B Bette Davis
C Betty Buckley
D Lady Bird Johnson

121 Who flew around the world in 91 hours, 14 minutes, setting a new world's record in 1938?

A Ross Perot, Jr.
B Chuck Yeager
C Charles Lindburgh
D Howard Hughes

122 Who designed the Shelby Mustang?

A Lee Iacocca
B Henry Ford IV
C Carroll Shelby
D John Wayne

123 What singer was killed in a plane crash near De Kalb on December 31, 1985?

A Buddy Holly
B Rick Nelson
C Sam Cooke
D Jim Croce

124 Which West Texas town did Marty Robbins make famous with a hit song?

A El Paso
B Port Arthur
C Odessa
D Honey Grove

125 Where did LBJ die?

A On a plane at Love Field
B In the White House
C At the LBJ Ranch
D At a dance hall near Luckenbach

126 Who was the Alabama quarterback in the 1968 Cotton Bowl Classic?

A Kenny Stabler
B Joe Namath
C Edd Hargett
D Steve Sloan

127 What SWC basketball team plays home games in a "drum"?

A Arkansas
B Baylor
C TCU
D Texas

128 What Texas car dealer was owner of the NBA Denver Nuggets?

A Frank Kent of Fort Worth
B Red McCombes of San Antonio
C Bill Dower of Corinth
D H.B. McCord of Tahoka

129 Which Kentucky Clipper called Dallas home at one point?

A Jack Daniels
B Secretariat
C Cliff Hagan
D Harlan Sanders

130 Name the movie in which John Travolta had a fling with the woman who later became the mother of Mick Jagger's child.

A "Peyton Place"
B "Urban Cowboy"

C "Welcome Back, Kotter"
D "Grease"

131 Where has Buddy Holly's widow, Maria Elena Holly Diaz, made her home over the past several years?
A Las Colinas
B Hollywood
C Nashville
D Lubbock

132 Who played Bobby Ewing in the TV series, "Dallas"?
A Mark Kohler
B Clay Bright
C Patrick Duffy
D Patrick Henry

133 What famous snack food was introduced in 1932 by a San Antonio man?
A Nachos
B Fritos
C Fried rattlesnake sticks
D Onion rings

134 The longest highway in Texas, U.S. 83, stretches 903 miles from which town to which?
A Texarkana to Texline
B Sherman to El Paso
C Plano to Duncanville
D Brownsville to Perryton

135 Socorro del sur, near El Paso, is the oldest ______ in America.

A Active Catholic parish
B Bartender
C Nudist Colony
D Soccer-style kicker

136 Where was Jack Ruby the moment President Kennedy was shot?

A Texas Schoolbook Depository, looking for Oswald
B Carousel Club in Dallas
C At *The Dallas Morning News,* placing an ad
D Skiing at Beaver Creek

137 Where did Fleet Admiral Chester Nimitz grow up?

A Fredericksburg
B Fort Hood
C River Oaks
D Kerrville

138 What is a Texas Ruby Red?

A A Bloody Mary with a double shot of tequila
B A grapefruit
C A member of Christopher Cross' back-up band
D The house special at the Chicken Ranch in LaGrange

139 In what capacity did former Texas Governor John Connally serve President Richard Nixon?

A Secretary of Barbeque
B Secretary of Defense
C Secretary of Treasury
D Secretary of Auctions

140 What is the official Texas State Dish?
A Chili
B Beef enchiladas
C Cabrito
D Goff's #2 with cheese

141 Name the Texas State Park which floats.
A L.B. Houston Flood Plains Park
B The Battleship *Texas*
C Lake Buchanan State Park
D Wet 'N Wild State Park

142 Which of the Monkees was from Dallas?
A Davey Jones
B Mickey Dolenz
C Peter Tork
D Michael Nesmith

143 "Vietnam Blues" was the first song written and recorded by:
A Willie Nelson
B Merle Haggard
C George Strait
D Kris Kristofferson

144 Blind Lemmon Jefferson is regarded as one of the important ______ men of Texas music.

A Blues
B Public Relations
C Rockabilly
D Heavy Metal

145 What Texas city has a Presidential Library?
A Sealy
B Austin
C Denison
D Bonham

146 Before Texas International merged with Continental Airlines, what was Texas International's previous name?
A Lone Star Air
B Trans Texas Airlines
C Braniff International
D Hughes Air West

147 Name Texas' largest mammal.
A Randy White
B E-Bar-S Cattle
C American Buffalo
D Bevo

148 What nationally-known drink was invented at the Cadillac Bar in Nuevo Laredo?
A Margarita
B Ramos Gin Fizz
C Tequila Sunrise
D Run, Jump, Skip and Go Naked

149 What fraternity did John Denver pledge at Texas Tech?

A Delta Delta Delta
B Delta Tau Delta
C Tau Delta Tau
D Tau Tau Tau

150 Who wrote the song, "True Love Ways"?
A Peter and Gordon
B Chad and Jeremy
C Mickey Gilley
D Buddy Holly

151 Who was Texas commander at the Battle of the Alamo?
A Davy Crockett
B William Barret Travis
C John Wayne
D Deaf Smith

152 The most famous Texas honky-tonk not located in Texas is called what?
A Hard Rock Cafe in London
B Lone Star Cafe in New York City
C Emmaline and Hessie's, St. Simons Island, Georgia
D Harold's Cafe Creek Corral at Cave Creek, Arizona

153 In the 1952 Texas state elections, what was the hot issue?
A Liquor-by-the-drink
B Tidelands mineral rights
C No pass, no play
D Secession

154 Where is Texas' White Buffalo statue?
A Snyder
B Buffalo Gap
C Canyon
D Joe Ferguson's living room

155 What Texas developer had the Oklahoma City Symphony Orchestra play at his son's wedding?
A Danny Faulkner
B Trammell Crow
C Sid Bass
D Gerald Hines

156 Where did Lenel Genter live when he was arrested in connection with some fast food store robberies?
A South Carolina
B Balch Springs, Texas
C Greenville, Texas
D Dallas, Texas

157 What does the Spanish word "cerveza" mean?
A Hello, how are you, nice to see you
B Can you tell me where Boys Town is?
C Service with a smile
D Beer

158 During the summer of 1985, what large family-owned specialty store, based in Houston, declared bankruptcy and closed most of its stores?
A Sakowitz

B Macy's
C Thomas and Hart
D Chudej's of Engle

159 What family lives at the King Ranch?
A Addams Family
B Sly and the Family Stone
C The Klebergs
D Sky and the Family King

160 Name Willie Nelson's long-time lead guitarist.
A Jody Payne
B Ray Price
C Al Bettis
D Stevie Ray Vaughan

161 What Houston dentist became a sports agent then became an owner of the USFL Houston franchise?
A Jimmy May
B Jerry Argovitz
C Clinton Manges
D George Jarman

162 Guich Koock is a well-known personality from which Texas Hill Country town?
A Galveston
B Bandera
C Leakey
D Fredericksburg

163 Who was Dallas' "Mayor of Ross Avenue"?

A Erik Jonsson
B Gene Goss, the Tradin' Hoss
C Shannon Wynne
D Ross Love

164 Where did Dandy Don Meredith go to college?
A Southern California
B Navy
C Texas Christian
D Southern Methodist

165 Who wrote the song, "The Eyes of Texas are Upon You"?
A John Lang Sinclair
B Jere Thompson
C J. Frank Dobie
D Steven Fromholtz

166 Who made the famous bench tackle of Dicky Maegle of Rice in the 1954 Cotton Bowl Classic?
A Mike South of Rice
B Tommy Lewis of Alabama
C Bill Forester of SMU
D Roger Staubach of Navy

167 Who did T. Cullen Davis of Fort Worth marry following his divorce from Priscilla Davis?
A Bubbles Cash
B Amanda Blake (Miss Kitty on "Gunsmoke")
C Karen Master
D Mrs. Racehorse Haynes

168 What Texan wrote "Trip to Bountiful"?
A Cindy Brinker
B Horton Foote
C Babs Greyhosky
D Sam Grogg

169 Where is the South Plains Mall?
A Tyler
B San Angelo
C Canyon
D Lubbock

170 Identify William Royce Scaggs.
A First man to die in the electric chair in Texas
B Founder of a large pharmacy/grocery store chain
C Singer Boz Scaggs
D Ricky Skaggs' twin brother

171 Name the first Texas university to win the GE College Bowl on TV.
A University of Texas at El Paso
B Texas Southern
C Rice
D Sul Ross

172 Where in Houston was the original Ninfa's opened?
A Westheimer
B Navigation Street
C On Hwy 1960 near I-45
D In the Galleria

173 What is the largest game bird in Texas?
A Ostrich

B Buzzard
C Wild Turkey
D Red Spotted Texas Megaduck

174 Texas has 624 miles of ______.
A Rivers
B Seashore
C Bicycle trails
D Farm to Market roads

175 Texas A&M is the only university in Texas offering a degree in:
A Oceanography
B Fish camping
C Cheerleader combat
D Aggie Jokalogy

176 What airline was created to compete with Southwest Airlines?
A People Express
B Muse Air
C American Eagle
D Continental Airlines

177 Where is Stroh beer brewed in Texas?
A San Antonio
B Tyler
C Longview
D Waco

178 Panna Maria is the oldest settlement in Texas for what group of settlers from Europe?
A Polish
B Portuguese

C South Africans
D Spanish

179 Weslaco, Texas, has the world's smallest what?
A TV tower
B Cafe
C Museum
D Mayor

180 What Texas NBA team made the finals of the NBA playoffs in 1981?
A Dallas Chaparrals
B Houston Rockets
C San Antonio Spurs
D Dallas Mavericks

181 Where is *Texas Football* magazine, the Lone Star state's Bible of the gridiron, published each year?
A Waco
B Arlington
C Midland/Odessa
D Temple

182 Who is Carrie Fisher's mother?
A Mrs. Darth Vader
B Debbie Reynolds
C Jerry Hall
D Carol Burnett

183 Who wrote the hit country song, "Crazy"?
A Patsy Cline
B Jerry Jeff Walker

C Guy Clark
D Willie Nelson

184 What opened in 1915 and fueled Houston's rapid economic growth?
A Astroworld
B Hobby Airport
C The Port of Houston
D The Southwest Freeway

185 When de Leon discovered the remains of LaSalle's ill-fated French colony in Texas in 1689, what did he find still there that was important?
A Imported French croussaints
B Two survivors
C Twenty cases of Bordeaux
D A replica of the Eiffel Tower

186 What is the translation of Wally Gonzales' song, "Tire mi Suegra al Rio"?
A "The Eyes of Texas are Upon You"
B "Take This Job and Shove It"
C "You're My Sugar Tire all the Live Long Days"
D "I Threw My Mother-in-Law in the River"

187 How old was Janis Joplin when she died?
A 16
B 21
C 27
D 34

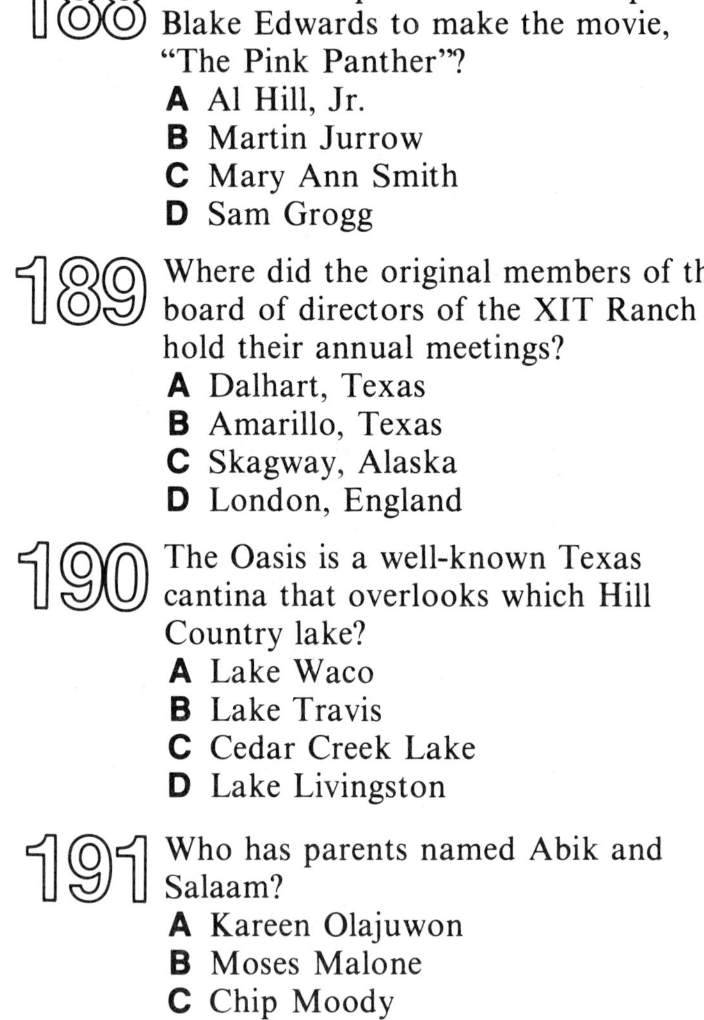

188 What Dallas producer teamed up with Blake Edwards to make the movie, "The Pink Panther"?

A Al Hill, Jr.
B Martin Jurrow
C Mary Ann Smith
D Sam Grogg

189 Where did the original members of the board of directors of the XIT Ranch hold their annual meetings?

A Dalhart, Texas
B Amarillo, Texas
C Skagway, Alaska
D London, England

190 The Oasis is a well-known Texas cantina that overlooks which Hill Country lake?

A Lake Waco
B Lake Travis
C Cedar Creek Lake
D Lake Livingston

191 Who has parents named Abik and Salaam?

A Kareen Olajuwon
B Moses Malone
C Chip Moody
D Fred Akers

192 What is the location of the free world's largest armored center?

A Armadillo World Headquarters
B Luckenbach

C Fort Hood
D Harvey Goff's backyard

193 What South Texas town is famous for Spindletop's oil gusher?
A Magnolia
B Beaumont
C San Augustine
D Port Aransas

194 Name the Rice star (with the French name) who in the late 60's was a defensive back and kick return specialist for the St. Louis Cardinals.
A Gary Hammond
B Pierre Toussaint
C Freddy Fender
D Chuck Latourette

195 What SWC football team plays home games at The Clifford B. and Audrey Jones Stadium?
A Houston Cougars
B Texas Tech Red Raiders
C Arkansas Razorbacks (what are they doing in a Texas book?)
D Baylor Bears

196 Which is a guitar player for Houston's legendary rock and roll band, ZZ Top?
A Dusty Hill
B Frank Beard
C Kinky Friedman
D Kathy Whitmire

197 What was the battlecry of the Texans at the Battle of San Jacinto?
A "Fight, Texas, Fight!"
B "Gig 'em Aggies!"
C "Remember the Alamo!"
D "Adios, Amigos!"

198 Identify gachupines.
A Leggings worn by cowboys out in the brush
B Spaniards — born in Spain — living in the new world
C The hot thing on the top of nachos
D Sandels worn by Padre Island beach bums

199 What is Tom Landry's hat size?
A 7¼
B 8
C 8½
D 12

200 Howard Hughes built an airplane called *Hercules* in 1947. What did most people actually call it?
A P-38
B *The Spirit of Houston*
C *The Spruce Goose*
D *The Space Shuttle*

201 What foreign country sends the second most tourists to Texas?
A Mexico
B England

C Canada
D Luxemburg

202 In what city was Neiman-Marcus founded?
A Garland
B Dallas
C Irving
D Fort Worth

203 What is the largest school in the state?
A The University of Texas at Austin
B Plano High School
C North Texas State University
D Texas Tech University

204 Where was the postal service initiated in Texas?
A El Paso
B San Felipe
C Houston
D La Grange

205 What school leads the world in petroleum engineer degrees?
A Kilgore Junior College
B The University of Texas at Austin
C Lubbock Christian College
D Texas A&M University

206 Who was not part of the Luckenbach revival:
A Guich Kooch
B Kathy Morgan
C Hondo Crouch
D Mean Joe Greene

207 Who was the first U.S. Congressman to don a uniform in World War II?

A Lyndon Johnson
B Steve Bartlett
C Henry Gonzales
D Spiro Agnew

208 Name the United States' 1846-1848 international war.

A Spanish-American War
B Mexican-American War
C War of 1812
D Texas-OU Weekend

209 Who makes $15 per game during the home Dallas Cowboys games?

A Crazy Ray
B Bum Bright
C The Dallas Cowboys Cheerleaders
D The referees

210 *The Texas Gazette* was the first __________ newspaper in Texas.

A Times-Mirror
B Yellow journalism
C All-sports
D Anglo

211 What is Tom Landry's favorite Mexican food restaurant?

A Papacita's
B Joe T. Garcia's
C Mia's
D Juanita's

212 Who recorded an album called, "Bat Out of Hell"?

A Pat Boone
B Meatloaf
C Asleep at the Wheel
D The Fabulous Thunderbirds

213 What Lubbock native starred in "North Dallas Forty"?

A Donny Anderson
B Joe Ely
C Mac Davis
D Kent Hance

214 What Texas governor invited everyone in the state to his daughter's wedding and had 25,000 take him up on it?

A W. Lee "Pappy" O'Daniel
B Bill Clements
C Dolph Briscoe
D Sam Houston

215 What Dallasite is the most famous black country singer of all time?

A Tony Joe Dorsett
B John Wiley Price
C Charley Pride
D Brice Beaird

216 Where is the world's tallest windmill commemorated?

A Guadalupe Peak
B InterFirst Plaza in Dallas
C Littlefield
D Amarillo

217 Where is the world's largest synthetic rubber manufacturing plant?

A Houston (Goodyear Tire and Rubber Co.)
B Brownwood (Daniel Baker Rubber Co.)
C Ft. Worth Stockyards
D DeSoto (Thorntree Manufacturing Co.)

218 What Illinois corporation brought Braniff back from bankrupcy?

A JMB Realty
B Hyatt Corporation
C Sears
D Playboy Enterprises, Inc.

219 What does M.K.T. stand for?

A Mary Kay Training
B Missouri, Kansas and Texas (railroad)
C Magnificent Katy Trains
D Machinegun Kelly's Texas

220 Which of the following are poisonous snakes found in Texas?

A Rattlesnake
B Coral snake
C Copperhead
D Water moccasin (Cottonmouth)

221 Where are the Chisos Mountains?

A Between Levelland and Plainview
B Texas Hill Country

C South of Corpus Christi
D Big Bend

222 Where is Miller Beer brewed in Texas?
A Fort Worth
B Marshall
C San Antonio
D Eastland

223 What was the first new cattle breed developed in America?
A Santa Gertrudis
B Longhorn
C Brahman
D Beefalo

224 One of the first two shopping centers in America is still flourishing in Texas. What is its name?
A Galleria in Houston
B Alamo Plaza in San Antonio
C Highland Park Shopping Village in Dallas
D Old Town in Dallas

225 In the movie, "Giant," what was Jordan Benedict II's nickname?
A Junior
B Bubba
C Little Rocky Two
D Bick

226 What country music legend from Crisp, Texas, died on September 6, 1984?
A Ernest Tubb

B Hank Williams
C Bob Wills
D Marvin Gaye

227 What major league baseball player hit the center field speaker at the Astrodome with a fair ball?
A Pete Rose
B Mike Schmidt
C Sandy Koufax
D Billy Martin

228 What large stadium in Texas has a partial roof?
A Amon Carter Stadium in Fort Worth
B Rice Stadium in Houston
C Texas Stadium in Irving
D Loos Stadium in Dallas

229 Which town was not a site of a Cullen Davis trial:
A Fort Worth
B Austin
C Amarillo
D Houston

230 Who bought the Dallas Cowboy's old practice field on Forest Lane?
A Lamar Hunt
B Roger Staubach
C Bobby Layne
D Norm Hitzges

231 When the Chicken Ranch in La Grange was shut down, who was the Fayette

County Sheriff?
A Sheriff Jim Flournoy
B Sheriff Jim Ed Dobbs
C Marshall Matt Dillon
D Sheriff Jim Bowles

232 For years, this Austin-based musical group has been noted for its western swing.
A The Nelsons
B The Lost Gonzo Band
C Asleep at the Wheel
D The Fabulous Thunderbirds

233 Former Houston Rocket standout Calvin Murphy won what unusual NCAA title while he was at Niagra?
A Syncronized swimming
B Baton twirling
C Slam Dunk contest
D Beer chugging

234 Odessa has a replica of what old theatre in England?
A The Globe Theatre
B The Majestic Theatre
C Ford's Theatre
D The Northtown Six Theatres

235 What was the name of the Miss USA who attended Texas A&M?
A Kim Tomes
B Farrah Fawcett
C Phyllis George
D Debra Sue Maffet

236 What Texas rocker has always been known for his dark glasses and slicked back hair?
A Tom Landry
B Van Cliburn
C Roy Orbison
D Bum Phillips

237 Who was second in command of the Rough Riders?
A Dwight Eisenhower
B Lee Simpson
C Franklin D. Roosevelt
D Teddy Roosevelt

238 *Horseman, Pass By,* a novel by Texan Larry McMurtry, was made into a movie (starring Paul Newman) called what?
A "The Sting"
B "Hud"
C "Butch Cassidy and the Sundance Kid"
D "Horseman, Pass By"

239 What Palestine native starred for the Texas Longhorns, then was all-pro for the Philadelphia Eagles?
A James Street
B Earl Campbell
C Doug English
D Bill Bradley

240 Who won the 1967 SWC football crown?

A Texas A&M
B Rice
C Texas Tech
D TCU

241 A famous meteor crater, near Interstate 20, is located next to what West Texas town?

A Dumas
B Odessa
C Van Horn
D Presidio

242 Who was the Colt's leading rusher in the 1970 Super Bowl. He was a former TCU standout.

A Mike Renfro
B Davey O'Brien
C Norm Bulaich
D Eugene "Goo" Kennedy

243 Who presented H. Ross Perot with the Winston Churchill Award in February, 1986?

A Winston Churchill
B J.R. Ewing
C The Prince of Wales
D The Duke of Ellington

244 What was the first TV station in Texas?

A WBAP, Fort Worth
B KHOU, Houston
C WFAA, Dallas
D KMAC, Lubbock

Texas honeydew melons are ripe when their skin turns what color?

A Black
B Brown
C Blue
D Deep yellow

246 Which of these former SMU athletes is a member of the NFL Hall of Fame?

A Louie Kelcher
B Kit Case
C Eric Dickerson
D Lamar Hunt

In 1978 what was the wealthiest city in Texas, in terms of per capita income?

A Houston
B Dallas
C Austin
D Midland

248 What former Texas Longhorn quarterback married Tom Landry's daughter?

A Rob Moerschell
B James Street
C Eddie Phillips
D Rick McIvor

249 What is named for Texan Oscar Pierce?

A Pierce-Arrow motorcar
B The Academy Awards' "Oscar"

C A brand of hot dogs
D A town near Waco

250 What West Texas town has had radio stations with the call letters KOYL and KRIG?
A Midland
B Odessa
C Lubbock
D Big Spring

251 Who was the first woman in Texas to be elected to the U.S. Congress?
A Janis Joplin
B Frances "Sissy" Farenthold
C Barbara Jordan
D Nancy Lieberman

252 What is housed in the largest garage on I-45, just north of Houston?
A The Confederate Air Force
B Goodyear blimp
C The *Spruce Goose*
D "Too Tall" Jones' brother-in-law's Cadillac

253 Name the only Texas governor to die while in office.
A Jack Ruby
B Beauford Jester
C Price Daniel
D Joe A. Irwin

254 Name the Rice coach from the mid-20's who had a trophy named for him.

A Oscar Meyer
B John Heisman
C John "Trophy" Dodson
D Ben Hogan

255 Who are the two Dallas Cowboy quarterbacks who have each cut a record?
A Don Meredith
B Thomas "Hollywood" Henderson
C Danny White
D Eddie LeBaron

256 What was Hank Thompson's hometown?
A Lubbock
B Corpus Christi
C Turkey
D Waco

257 Which of the following rivers is *not* a border for Texas?
A Red
B Colorado
C Rio Grande
D Sabine

258 Who was the first President of the Republic of Texas?
A Sam Houston
B David G. Burnet
C Fritz Von Erich
D Mirabeau Lamar

259 Who was the Dallas police officer slain by Lee Harvey Oswald?

A J.D. Tippit
B Jack Ruby
C Henry Wade
D Erik Estrada

260 What Pasadena nightclub was voted "Nightclub of the Year" by the Academy of Country Music in 1983 and 1984?
A Billy Bob's Texas
B Soap Creek
C Gilley's
D Coldwater Cattle Company

261 What office did Dolph Briscoe, Jr. hold that his father also held?
A Governor of the Great State of Texas
B Tail Twister in the Lions Club
C President of the Southwest Cattle Raiser's Association
D First vice-president of the Uvalde PTA Dad's committee

262 What bootmaker did Jerry Jeff Walker immortalize in song?
A Charlie Dunn
B Hondo Crouch
C Kenneth Threadgill
D Peta Nocona

263 What Texan holds the record for the most Indianapolis 500 wins?
A Carrol Shelby
B A.J. Foyt

C Johnny Rutherford
D Elvin "The Big E" Hayes

264 Who was the only woman to be elected governor of Texas?
A Lady Bird Johnson
B Miriam "Ma" Ferguson
C Dolphinia Briscoe
D Mrs. William Hobby

265 Who defeated the Aztecs in the 16th century?
A The Incas
B The Houston Oilers
C Interest rates
D The Spanish

266 What was Johnny Ringo's real name?
A Richard Starkey
B Johnny Eckeberger
C Johnny Ringgold
D Jonathon Rutherford Ringo III

267 Who was the character played by James Dean in "Giant"?
A Jett Rink
B Bick Benedict
C Danny Noonan
D J.R. Ewing

268 What Texas town has an Astrodome?
A San Angelo
B Irving
C Conroe
D Houston

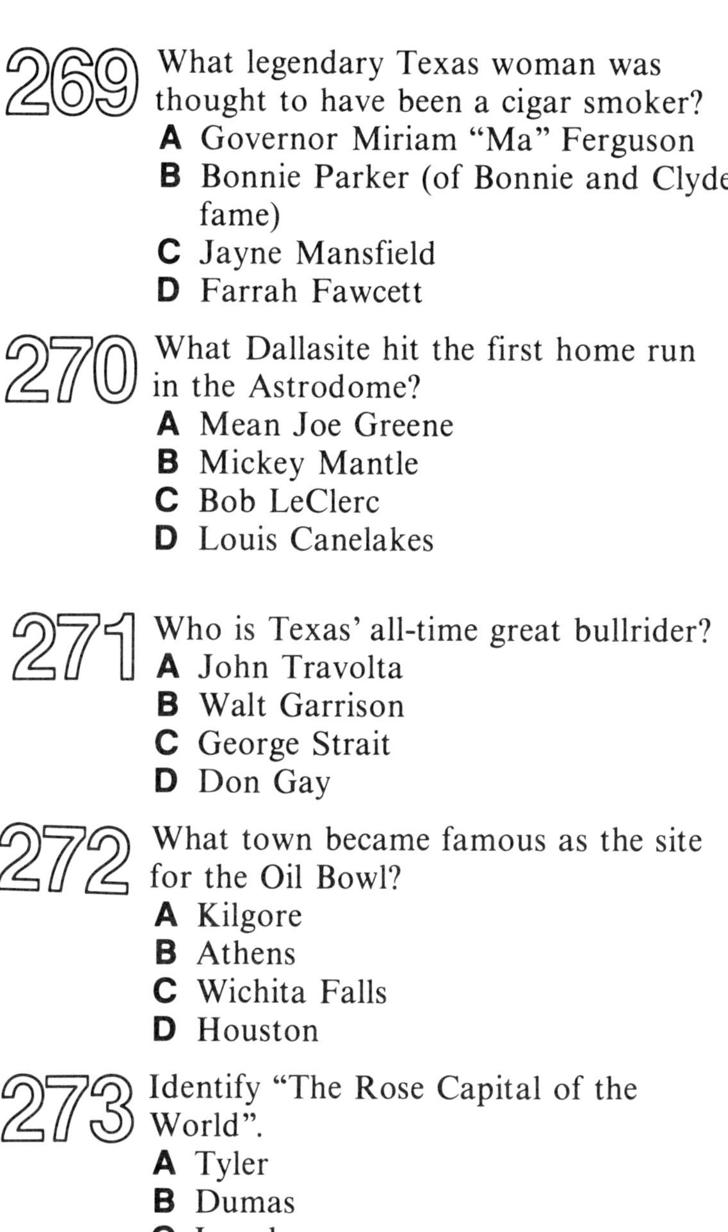

269 What legendary Texas woman was thought to have been a cigar smoker?

A Governor Miriam "Ma" Ferguson
B Bonnie Parker (of Bonnie and Clyde fame)
C Jayne Mansfield
D Farrah Fawcett

270 What Dallasite hit the first home run in the Astrodome?

A Mean Joe Greene
B Mickey Mantle
C Bob LeClerc
D Louis Canelakes

271 Who is Texas' all-time great bullrider?

A John Travolta
B Walt Garrison
C George Strait
D Don Gay

272 What town became famous as the site for the Oil Bowl?

A Kilgore
B Athens
C Wichita Falls
D Houston

273 Identify "The Rose Capital of the World".

A Tyler
B Dumas
C Laredo
D Hurst-Euless-Bedford

274 What was the nickname of Hardin-Simmons All-American Clyde Turner?
A "Clyde the Glide"
B "Bulldog"
C "The Mouth of the South"
D "White Shoes"

275 What was Buddy Holly's real full name?
A Charles Hardin Holly
B Charles Hardin
C Buddy Hardin
D Charles Hardin Holley

276 It was the last fight of its kind, back in 1881. What was it?
A AFS vs NFL
B Last Indian fight in Texas
C Bare knuckle heavyweight championship
D Texas-OU game in Oklahoma

277 Who was the "Father of Texas"?
A Bill Clements
B Stephen F. Austin
C Davy Crockett
D Jim Bowie

278 What university has been located in Tehuancana, Waxahachie and San Antonio?
A Trinity
B University of Texas at San Antonio
C Tehuancana Tech
D Waxahachie Junior College

279 What is Texas' lowest point of elevation?

A Guadalupe Peak
B The Gulf Coast line
C Odessa
D The bottom of the Hill Country

280 On whose birthday was the outlaw Sam Bass killed?

A His own
B Lincoln's Birthday
C The man who killed him
D Sid Richardson's

281 What is Joe Bob Brigg's favorite type of motion picture?

A G-rated
B Foreign
C Drive-In
D Walt Disney

282 What Dallas Cowboy receiver went on to become a successful novelist?

A Bob Hayes
B Butch Johnson
C Drew Pearson
D Peter Gent

283 What happened to Texas on January 3, 1959?

A Darrell Royal met Willie Nelson for the first time
B A tornado touched down in the eye of a hurricane
C Texas became the second largest

state in the union

D Buddy Holly's plane crashed on the "day the music died"

284 Where is the Four States Fair held?

A Dalhart

B Texarkana

C El Paso

D There's no such animal

285 What battle is reinacted in Laredo?

A Battle of the Bulge

B Battle of Laredo

C Battle Against Infectious Diseases

D Battle of the Alamo

286 Name the legendary high school football coach from Brownwood who retired after the 1985 season.

A "Tugboat" Jones

B Gordon Wood

C Tom Landry

D Frank Bevers

287 If your team is playing against the "Mojo", who are you playing?

A Exorcist Polytech

B Plano Wildcats

C Odessa Permian

D Denison Yellow Jackets

288 Which of the following songs did *not* make the 1980 top 10 in both country and contemporary music?

A "Drivin' My Life Away" by Eddie Rabbitt

B "Lookin' For Love" by Johnny Lee
C "Lady" by Kenny Rogers
D "She Got the Gold Mine, and I Got the Shaft," by Jerry Reed

289 Robert Redford, Jane Fonda and Willie Nelson all starred in what movie?
A "Electric Horseman"
B "Butch Cassidy and the Sundance Kid"
C "On Golden Pond"
D "Behind the Green Door"

290 SMU theatre graduate James McLure wrote what successful play, involving a pink Thunderbird convertible?
A "Tan Shoes and a Pink Carnation"
B "Lone Star"
C "77 Sunset Strip"
D "The Last Drive-in Picture Show"

291 This Port Arthur native was the lead singer for Big Brother and the Holding Company.
A Tina Turner
B Janis Joplin
C Phyllis George
D Mary Anna Austin

292 The U.S. House of Representatives building in Washington is named for what Texan?
A Lyndon B. Johnson
B Gene Street

C John Tower
D Sam Rayburn

293 When was the World's Fair held in San Antonio?
A 1970
B 1968
C 1966
D 1962

294 Clear Lake is the hometown for what world-famous organization?
A NASA
B The Houston Astros
C The Texas Barbershop Quartet Association
D CLO

295 When Bob Lilly retired from the Dallas Cowboys, what beer did he start selling?
A Lone Star
B Pearl
C Coors
D Shiner

296 Name the most recent Texan to win the Heisman Trophy.
A Billy Sims
B Doak Walker
C Earl Campbell
D Eric Dickerson

297 What head coach led the Houston Oilers to back-to-back AFC title games in 1979 and 1980?

A Bud Adams
B O.A. "Bum" Phillips
C Mike Renfro
D Guy Lewis

298 Who is the drummer for ZZ Top?
A Phil Collins
B Frank Beard
C Dusty Hill
D Billy Gibbons

299 Claude, Texas, was the site for what movie filmed in the early 60's?
A "The Billy Claude Story"
B "Giant"
C "East of Eden"
D "Hud"

300 What is the state bird of Texas?
A Whooping Crane
B Mockingbird
C Golden Eagle
D Buzzard

301 Where is the XIT Rodeo and Reunion held each year?
A Huntsville
B Dalhart
C Pecos
D Mesquite

302 What was the name of the Dallas soccer team owned by Lamar Hunt?
A Dallas Texans
B Dallas Sidekicks

C Dallas Tornado
D Austin American Statesmen

303 What Texas city gave the world football greats such as Bubba Smith, Tody Smith, Mel Farr, Miller Farr and Jerry Levias?
A Beaumont
B Monahans
C Plano
D Brownwood

304 Where was the movie, "The Texas Chainsaw Massacre" filmed?
A Hollywood
B Dallas
C Texarkana
D Round Rock

305 Wink is the hometown of what singer, known for "Pretty Woman"?
A Bobby Sherman
B Frank Zappa
C Ed Bernet
D Roy Orbison

306 Where is America's largest collection of flying-condition World War II aircraft?
A Harlingen (Confederate Air Force Museum)
B Houston (Southwest Airline's hangar at Hobby)
C Aboard the *U.S.S. Maine*
D Houston (in Howard Hughes' backyard)

307 What river feeds Possum Kingdom Lake?
A Brazos
B Red
C Trinity
D Mississippi

308 What Texas town has a name which means Virgin Mary?
A Panna Maria
B Lubbock
C Nuevo Laredo
D Juarez

309 Name one 825,000 acre ranch in Texas.
A King Ranch
B Queen Ranch
C Las Colinas
D Spade and Spur in Oakland

310 The "Nose Society" has been a tradition at what Texas school?
A Houston Wheatley
B UT-San Antonio
C Baylor
D Temple High

311 Texas guitarist Stevie Ray Vaughan played on whose album, "Let's Dance"?
A Michael Jackson
B Joe Bob Briggs
C Fred Astaire
D David Bowie

312 Name the first turnpike in Texas.
A Preston Trail

B El Camino Real
C Martin Luther King Tollway
D Dallas-Fort Worth Turnpike

313 The Buckaroos have backed him up. Name this Texas legend.
A Captain Kangaroo
B Buck Owens
C Gary Hogeboom
D Willie Nelson

314 What movie did Peter Bogdanovich shoot in black and white in Texas?
A "Paper Moon"
B "The Dallas Cowboy Cheerleaders"
C "The Last Picture Show"
D "The Wizard of Oz"

315 What was Jayne Mansfield's real name?
A Grace Suk
B Jane Bob Goldstein
C Vera Jane Peers
D Elvira Snorklepoop

316 Name the "National Beer of Texas."
A Lone Star
B Pearl
C Shiner
D JR Beer

317 The name "Texas" comes from the Indian word "Tejas." What does Tejas mean?
A Texas
B The god of Football

C Friends
D Land of Black Gold

318 Super Bowl XX, in 1986, featured what two former Dallas Cowboy coaches?
A Mike Ditka
B Duane Thomas
C Raymond Berry
D Raymond Dyer

319 Who is credited with sewing the first Texas flag?
A Laura Ashley
B Susanne Dickenson
C Sarah Dodson
D Ralph Lauren

320 Who is "Big Tex"?
A Middle linebacker for the Houston Oilers
B A wealthy Midland oilman who flies an Aggie flag on top of his building
C The official greeter of the State Fair of Texas in Dallas
D An El Paso bail bondsman who has no last name

321 Who searched for the Seven Cities of Cibola?
A Thomas "Hollywood" Henderson
B Francisco Vazquez de Coronado
C Amon Carter
D Alvar Nunez Cabeza de Vaca

322 Identify Garrett Breedlove.
A Role played by Jack Nicholson in

"Terms of Endearment"
B Famous jet-car driver from Muleshoe, Texas
C San Antonio's top polo player
D Farrah Fawcett's high school boyfriend

323 Who was the first American astronaut in outer space?
A John Glenn
B Alan Shepard
C George Jetson
D David Clyde

324 Where was the movie "Giant" filmed?
A Marfa
B Claude
C Abilene
D Austin

325 What two men started the Prufrock restaurant chain, featuring "Black Eyed Pea" and "Dixie House" restaurants?
A Gene Street
B Phil Cobb
C Greg Price
D Honest Tom Stephenson

326 Name the warmest town in Texas.
A Dalhart
B Amarillo
C Dumas
D Presidio

327 What was the name of Tex Ritter's horse?

A Suzanne Sommers
B Fury
C White Flash
D Rin Tin Tin

328 Name the two U.S. Presidents who were born in Texas.
A Lyndon Johnson
B Abraham Lincoln
C Theodore Roosevelt
D Dwight Eisenhower

329 After he was killed, whose body was brought to Dallas' Belo Mansion (then a funeral home) as thousands of onlookers gathered?
A Howard Hughes
B President John F. Kennedy
C Deena the Chimp
D Gangster Clyde Barrow

330 What did the HemisFair in San Antonio celebrate?
A The invention of sizzling fajitas
B San Antonio's 250th anniversary
C Texas' 100th anniversary
D The Alamo survivors reunion

331 When did Austin's Scholz Beer Garten open?
A 1966
B 1936
C 1906
D 1866

332 Name the Robstown, Texas, native who became the first NFL player to appear in Super Bowls spanning three decades.
A Bob Lilly
B Gene Upshaw
C Chuck Howley
D Abner Haynes

333 What Washington Redskin lineman conducted a running feud with Roger Staubach?
A Diron Talbert
B Joe Theisman
C George Allen
D John Riggins

334 What country singer lives just south of Dallas and has buffalo on her ranch?
A Janie Fricke
B Barbara Mandrell
C Dolly Parton
D Tanya Tucker

335 John Graves' classic book, *Goodbye to a River,* features which Texas river?
A Brazos
B Guadalupe
C Colorado
D Pecos

336 Name the fifth flag to fly over Texas.
A France
B The Confederacy

C Texas
D The United States

337 What Speaker of the Texas House of Representatives was the son of a former governor?
A Gib Lewis
B Price Daniel, Jr.
C Preston Smith
D Sam Rayburn

338 What event prompted the Spanish to launch 11 expeditions into the Texas area in the late 1680's?
A Coronado discovered oil
B The death of Christopher Columbus
C LaSalle's French settlement in Texas
D Interest rates were down

339 Name the first female mayor of Houston.
A Debra Winger
B Kathy Whitmire
C Barbara Jordan
D Oveta Culp Hobby

340 Who drove the pace car in the 1984 Dallas Grand Prix?
A Buddy Boren
B A.J. Foyt
C Carroll Shelby
D Lee Iacocca

341 What foreign country sends the most tourists to Texas?

A Oklahoma
B Canada
C Mexico
D Iceland

342 Who wrote *The Best Little Whorehouse in Texas?*
A Jim Flournoy
B Gary Cartwright
C Larry L. King
D Marvin Zindler

343 What Bloomington, Texas, native starred in "My Little Margie"?
A Margie Herbert
B Marj Waters
C Marie Osmond
D Gale Storm

344 The Gulf Freeway goes from the Gulf of Mexico to what city?
A Longview
B Houston
C Mexico City
D Seminole

345 "Everybody's Somebody in __________"
A Luckenbach
B Huntsville Federal Prison
C San Antonio
D Dumas

346 What do you call a fly ball that lands safely between the infield and the outfield?

A Texas Leaguer
B Texas Ranger defense
C Home run
D Frozen rope

347 Former Dallas car dealer Ted Cassidy played what role as the butler in "The Addams Family" on television?
A Cousin It
B Lurch
C Thing
D Benson

348 What did Elmer Doolin invent?
A Cowboy boots
B Elmer's glue
C Barbed wire
D Frito's

349 Who lives at Toad Hall in Amarillo?
A Stanley Marsh 3
B T. Boone Pickens
C Dan Lokey
D David Nail

350 What is the highest town in Texas, at 5,450 feet?
A Austin
B Frijole
C Texline
D Study Butte

351 Jack Adkisson is the patriarch of what world-famous family?
A The Von Erichs
B The Von Trapps

C The Partridge Family
D The Fort Worth Bass family

352 Name the small town near Abilene where residents formerly had to go to buy beer, wine and liquor.
A Buffalo Gap
B Impact
C Baird
D Sweetwater

353 What is the largest church in Texas, in terms of congregation?
A Church on the Rock in Rockwall
B St. Mark's in Houston
C First Baptist Church in Dallas
D Astrodome Presbyterian

354 Who was TCU's Heisman Trophy winner?
A Kenneth Davis
B Sammy Baugh
C Bob Lilly
D Davey O'Brien

355 Who was the SMU football coach who left to coach the New England Patriots?
A Doak Walker
B Sean Stopperich
C E.O. "Doc" Hayes
D Ron Meyer

356 What was William O. Frizzell's nickname?
A "Stinky"

B "Frizzy"
C "Lefty"
D "Dr. F"

357 What movie was filmed in McKinney?
A "Benji"
B "Animal House"
C "Debbie Does McKinney"
D "Stand Alone"

358 What is TAERF?
A Texas Alcoholism Enemies Reform Fund
B Total All-out Energy Rejuvenescence Festival
C The Abilene Energy Research Foundation
D Texas Atomic Energy Research Foundation

359 In terms of size, what is the largest state in the U.S.?
A Texas
B California
C Alaska
D Montana

360 What town once had 1,100 oil wells within its city limits?
A Plainview
B Kilgore
C Ranger
D Houston

361 Where is Monument Hill State Park?
A La Grange

B Monument Hill, Texas
C San Antonio
D Hereford

362 Lipans and Mescaleros are what?
A Diseases
B Apache Indians
C Texas-sized houseflies
D People who swim the Rio Grande

363 "99 guys and a doll" referred to what school's marching band?
A Austin's Reagan High
B SMU
C Sam Houston State
D Texas A&M

364 Who has been published as the greatest bartender in Dallas history?
A Judge Roy Bean
B Billy Bob Harris
C J.R. Ewing
D The late, great Joe Miller

365 In which historic Texas hotel were the Rough Riders organized?
A La Quinta in Lubbock
B Menger Hotel in San Antonio
C Shamrock Hotel in Houston
D Weimer Country Inn in Weimer

366 Where was famous Texas outlaw John Wesley Hardin fatally shot?
A Texas-OU game
B River Oaks Country Club's thirteenth green

C Belle Starr's hide-out
D In the back of the head

367 His recordings of "If I Had a Hammer" and "La Bamba" made this Dallas singer a star.
A Trini Lopez
B Mariano Martinez
C Paul Stookey
D Ray Wylie Hubbard

368 What is the turkey capital of Texas?
A Turkey, Texas
B Cuero, Texas
C College Station
D Waco

369 Who played Jim Bowie in the 1960 movie, "The Alamo"?
A John Wayne
B Richard Widmark
C Butch Strunk
D Chill Wills

370 How did country singing star Jim Reeves die at the age of 39?
A Old age
B Airplane crash
C Death by injection
D Football injury

371 In what 1969 film does Peter Ustinov portray a Mexican general who tries to recapture the Alamo?
A "Rocky"

B "The Alamo III"
C "Viva Max!"
D "Fast Times at Ridgemont High"

372 In 1968, the largest crowd to ever see a Texas basketball game gathered at the Astrodome to see which two teams play?
A University of Houston — UCLA
B Wheatley High — Strake Jesuit
C Q Morning Zoo-keepers — Houston Oilers
D Houston Rockets — Los Angeles Lakers

373 Who was the original Texas A&M 12th man (who came out of the stands to help the Aggies)?
A H.R. "Bum" Bright
B Shelby Metcalf
C King Gill
D Eddie Dominquez

374 What well-known Texas Longhorn receiver was known as "Cotton"?
A Charles Speyer
B Johnny "Lam" Jones
C Daryl Comer
D Manning Shannon

375 What is the name of the largest Texas State Chili Cookoff in San Marcos?
A Luckenbach Memorial Chili Cookoff
B Chilimpiad

C Sam Marcos World Championship
D Frank X. Tolbert Memorial

376 In what year was Dr. Pepper invented in Waco?
A 1985
B 1945
C 1905
D 1885

377 Name Lyndon and Lady Bird's two daughters.
A Luci Baines
B Trisha
C Lynda Bird
D Amy

378 In terms of population, what is the largest city in Texas?
A Dallas
B San Antonio
C Houston
D Oklahoma City

379 What is halfway between El Paso and Fort Worth along the Texas & Pacific Railroad?
A Midland
B Snyder
C Indians
D Cisco

380 Who said, "Millions of red-blooded Americans wanted to kill Oswald. Jack was there. That's all."

A Frank Reynolds on ABC-TV
B Dallas District Attorney Henry Wade
C Jack Ruby's sister, Ava Grant
D Dallas television journalist Bert Shipp

381 What was the name of Sam Houston's horse?
A Buttercup
B Clyde the Glide
C Saracen
D William B. Travis

382 Which of the following is *not* a cactus?
A Flapjack
B Mr. Telephone
C Cow's tongue
D Candy Barrel

383 Where were Bonnie and Clyde killed?
A Ennis, Texas
B Arcadia, Louisiana
C St. Joseph, Missouri
D Raton, New Mexico

384 Who was the first television meteorologist in Texas?
A Harold Taft, WBAP (now KXAS) in Fort Worth
B Donald Bowman, KHOU in Houston
C Tracy Elms, KMID in Midland
D Troy Dungan, WFAA in Dallas

What brand did Ab Blocker design?
A E-Bar-S
B XIT
C 6666
D 4UR

Where can a hungry Texan find a good chicken-fried lobster?
A Tyler Petroleum Club
B On the Border, Dallas
C Jorge's, Austin
D State Line, El Paso

What town was named by promoters who thought the area looked like the "Alps of Texas"?
A Slaton
B Alpine
C Kerrville
D Bandera

388 Who was the large New York Jet (from Texas Southern) who protected Joe Namath during the Jets' glory days?
A Emerson Boozer
B Don Maynard
C Winston Hill
D Mean Joe Green

389 Wichita Falls produced what world-famous race car driver?
A Carter King
B Johnny Rutherford
C Lloyd Ruby
D Lloyd Taylor, Jr.

390 Who killed Billy the Kid?

A His babysitter
B Bad News Barnes
C Pat Garrett
D Pat Snuffer

391 What Texas beer was known for its XXX?

A Pearl
B Texas Select
C Sugar free Shiner
D Secret prohibition brewski from Muenster

392 Identify "The Old Scotsman."

A Randy Emery
B Gordon McLendon
C Scott Verplank
D Michael Moroney

393 Who has been declared a lifetime distinguished visiting professor at SMU?

A Bobby Collins
B Jon Koncak
C Bob Hope
D Duane Bogie

394 What is the state motto?

A "Remember the Alamo!"
B "Friendship"
C "Speak Softly and Carry a Big H-Bomb"
D "What's the Line on Tonight's Game?"

Who is Andre the Giant?

A A bear in the San Antonio Zoo
B A professional wrestler
C This year's ugliest debutante in Houston
D Eugene Lockhart's poodle

396 What were the first eight words spoken on the Moon?

A "Who are all of these green people?"
B "Tastes Great! Less Filling! Tastes Great! Less. . . . "
C "Houston. Tranquility Base here. *The Eagle* has landed."
D "This is almost as wonderful as Texas"

397 When was the Alamo (San Antonio de Valero) founded?

A 1617
B 1718
C 1819
D 1920

398 Which Texan won the most PGA tour titles during his career?

A Scott Verplank
B Ben Hogan
C Lee Trevino
D Ben Crenshaw

399 What is the mascot of the El Paso baseball club in the Texas League?

A The Diablos
B The Margaritas

C The Sunburns
D The Cubs

400 The Battle of Sabine Pass occurred near what Texas town?
A Fort Stockton
B Breckenridge
C Beaumont
D Farmers Branch

401 Paul Newman and Walter Brennan have both portrayed in movies which legendary Texas "law and order" figure?
A Jay Armes
B Judge Roy Bean
C Police Woman
D Attorney General Jim Mattox

402 Where was the first French settlement in Texas?
A Six Flags Over Texas
B La Reunion
C Lavaca Bay
D Galveston

403 Why did Richard King, the founder of the King Ranch, come to Texas?
A To operate a steamboat during the Mexican-American War
B To invent the weedeater and sell the rights for $10,000,000
C He was looking for H.L. Hunt
D He ran away from home at the age of 11

404 Where did Mean Joe Greene go to college?

A TCU
B Baylor
C SMU
D North Texas State

405 Who pitched the first Houston Astro no-hitter?

A Scott Kelm (1973)
B Don Nottebart (1963)
C Tom Kennedy (1958)
D Nolan Ryan (1982)

406 Where was "The Last Picture Show" filmed?

A Archer City
B Gemini Theater in Dallas
C Austin
D Universal Studios, Los Angeles

407 The main building at which university in the state is named for the 28th governor?

A Baylor (Pat Neff Hall)
B SMU (Perkins Natatorium)
C Texas Tech (Preston Smith Coliseum)
D University of Houston (Elvin Hayes Hall)

408 What are Texas' two state holidays?

A San Jacinto Day
B Darrell Royal's birthday

C Texas Independence Day
D Cinco de Mayo

409 What did El Paso and Laredo have 20 years before Brownsville?
A Margaritas
B The U.S. Border Patrol
C A railroad
D A Marty Robbins song

410 What movie poster did Joe Buck have pasted on his wall in "Midnight Cowboy"?
A Cheryl Tiegs in a mesh bathing suit in an unknown movie
B "Hud"
C "Romeo and Juliet"
D "Splash!"

411 What television show featured an appearance by Gov. Mark White?
A "Jeopardy"
B "The Flintstones"
C "What's My Line?"
D "Dallas"

412 Where were Leon Jaworski and Steve Martin born?
A London, Texas
B Waco
C San Marcos
D Odessa

413 Why was Denton rancher Rex Cauble sent to prison?

A Selling cowboy boots at a 700% markup
B Betting against the Cowboys at home
C Masterminding the "Cowboy Mafia"
D Insider stock trading

414 What family is the impetus behind the El Chico restaurant chain?
A Cuellars of Dallas
B Gonzales of El Paso
C Cisneros of San Antonio
D Wallers of Albany

415 What Texas city has two major Breweries?
A Longview
B Houston
C San Antonio
D Texas City

416 How many people were killed at the Cullen Davis mansion the night of August 2, 1976?
A None
B One
C Two
D Three

417 Many policemen who chased Texas outlaw Clyde Barrow agreed that had he gone straight, he would have become a great what?
A Race car driver
B Bank teller

C Policeman
D Comedian

418 What UT-Austin graduate won an Oscar for his direction of "Kramer vs Kramer"?
A Jerry Kramer
B Robert Benton
C Walter Cronkite
D Ken Harrison

419 Frank X. Tolbert's book, *A Bowl of Red,* is about what subject in Texas?
A High school football
B Speaking in tongues along I-45
C Everything you ever wanted to know about cheerleading
D Chili

420 Name the high school star who led Bridge City to the AAA state championship in football in 1966, then starred for the Texas Longhorns.
A Roosevelt Leaks
B Steve Worster
C Jim Bertleson
D Earl Campbell

421 John "Bet a Million" Gates got his nickname in the 1870's when he bet his fortune that ________ would change the face of the West.
A The Cowboys drafting Roger Staubach
B Barbed wire

C Birth control
D Bottle openers

422 Where was "Urban Cowboy" filmed?
A Pasadena, Texas
B Burbank, California
C Santa Fe, New Mexico
D Fort Worth, Texas

Where did John Denver go to high school in Fort Worth?
A Paschal
B Western Hills
C Arlington Heights
D Dunbar

What is the name of the UT mascot?
A Peruna
B Happy
C Rooster Andrews
D Bevo

425 Name the longest river associated with Texas.
A Colorado
B Brazos
C Rio Grande
D Sabine

426 Who threw the pass to Randy Peschel when Texas beat Arkansas in the 1969 Big Shootout for the national championship?
A Alan Lowrey
B Eddie Phillips

C Jack Mildren
D James Street

427 What was Ernest Tubb's first hit song?
A "Walkin' the Floor Over You"
B "Waltz Across Texas"
C "San Antonio Rose"
D "Johnny, Are You Queer?"

428 What kind of food is pictured inside ZZ Top's "Tres Hombres" album cover?
A Chicken fried steak
B Mexican food galore
C Miles and miles of french fries
D 35 kilos of top grade chuck

429 What is the name of James Michener's book about Texas?
A *Lone Star*
B *Lonesome Dove*
C *Life Its Ownself*
D *Texas*

430 Where did the pirate Jean Lafitte establish his headquarters after he left New Orleans?
A La Grange
B Galveston
C Port Arthur
D South Padre Island

431 What Dallas Cowboy quarterback was known as the "Mad Bomber"?
A Don Meredith

B Clint Longley
C Gary Hogeboom
D Jerry Rhome

432 Who was the first Vice-President of the Republic of Texas?
A Lorenzo de Zavala
B George Bush
C Sam Houston
D Moses Austin

433 What is the largest state park in Texas?
A Palo Duro State Park
B Big Bend National Park
C Daingerfield State Park
D Garner State Park

434 What was Governor Preston Smith's wife's maiden name? Her first name is Ima.
A Ima Crozier
B Ima Hogg
C Ima Smith
D Ima Wrong

435 Why are the stores in Keene, Texas, closed on Saturdays?
A State Blue laws
B Everyone leaves town for the weekends
C It's a ghost town
D Keene was founded by Seventh Day Adventists

436 An estimated 5,000 people were killed in Galveston by a ________ in 1900.

A Riot in the Soccer stadium in Galveston
B Hurricane
C Tornado
D Chemical leak

437 What Texan is credited with introducing the frisbee to the island of Borneo?
A Steve Emly
B Art Mulligan
C Kinky Friedman
D Mac Davis

438 Clay Allison, the "Gentleman Gunfighter" of Texas, now buried in Pecos, has what inscription on his gravestone?
A "Lost in the Shuffle"
B "Rest in Pieces"
C "He Never Killed a Man Who Did Not Deserve Killing"
D "See Y'all Downstairs"

439 In the order of admission to the U.S., what number was Texas?
A First
B Twenty-eighth
C Forty-eighth
D Thirty-first

440 Where is the Ranching Heritage Museum?
A Lubbock
B Hurst-Euless-Bedford

C Conroe
D Denison

441 What unique art can be found at Hueco Tanks and Seminole Canyon?
A Billy Hassell's first watercolors
B Indian pictographs
C Richard Avedon's "Faces of West Texas"
D Stanley Marsh 3's Volkswagen collection

442 Where is Texas' only veterinary college?
A Richland College
B Texas Tech
C Sul Ross
D Texas A&M

443 Who recorded the hit song, "Amarillo by Morning"?
A George Strait
B David Card
C Stanley Marsh 3
D Merle Haggard

444 What river within the state is best known for its white water?
A Trinity
B Canadian
C Pecos
D Guadalupe

445 What Texas monument is 570 feet tall?
A Big Tex
B Kareem Olajuwon

C San Jacinto Monument
D Lufkin's Petrified Pear Tree

446 What Texas border town was founded in 1755?
A El Paso
B Laredo
C Texarkana
D Texline

447 What Galveston native was the first black heavyweight boxing champion?
A Wilson Whitley
B Tex Harrison
C Jack Johnson
D George Foreman

448 What was originally going to be the name of the Dallas Cowboys?
A The Dallas Texans
B The Dallas Chaparrals
C The Dallas Cowboys
D The Dallas Rangers

449 Which of the following Texas golfers has won three Masters?
A Lee Trevino
B Ben Crenshaw
C Don January
D Jimmy Demaret

450 Where was Mac Davis born and raised?
A Round Rock
B Crockett

C Duncanville
D Lubbock

451 Where is the battleship *USS Texas?*
A Stationed in the Greek Islands
B At the San Jacinto Battlefield
C They melted it down and sold it for scrap metal
D Still defending the Alamo

452 Who is Juanita Dale Slusher?
A Candy Barr
B Bubbles Cash
C Lady Bird Johnson
D The maid at the Chicken Ranch

453 Where was the first underground parking in Texas?
A The Petroleum Building in Houston
B Highland Park Shopping Village in Dallas
C La Mansion del Rio Hotel in San Antonio
D Behind the Store in Terlingua

454 What was Dale Evans' horse's name?
A Buttercup
B Buttermilk
C Butterfingers
D Old Paint

455 When does Willie Nelson love to throw a big picnic?
A Thanksgiving
B Fourth of July

C Memorial Day
D Opening day of dove season

456 Who wrote the song, "Desperados Waiting for a Train"?
A Guy Clark
B Townes Van Zant
C Jerry Jeff Walker
D Nobody

457 Who's single, "Big Bad John," sold over two million copies?
A Lorene Greene
B Jimmy Dean
C Brice Beaird
D John Niland

458 Who is the Texas mass murderer who killed Dean Corll?
A Candace Montgomery
B Elmer Wayne Henley
C Bigfoot
D Henry Lee Lucas

459 What did James Dean think of the movie "Giant" when he saw the first screening after its release?
A He threw his popcorn at the screen
B He pouted and made the girls go wild
C He was killed in a car wreck before the movie was released
D He ordered champagne for everyone in the theater

Who was the first Republican in modern Texas history to win a statewide election?

A William P. Clements
B Sam Houston
C Kent Hance
D John Tower

461 What hit Armen Terzian in the head in 1975?

A Halley's Comet
B A golf ball hit by President Ford
C A bottle thrown at the referee in the Cowboy-Viking game
D A hot air balloon full of cold air

462 Who is H.L. Hunt's eldest son?

A Nelson Bunker
B William Herbert
C Hassie
D Lamar

What is the number one use for Astroturf?

A Football fields
B Pool and deck areas
C Experimental cattle grazing
D Fairways at Middle East country clubs

Who was the Houston socialite who died mysteriously and was the subject of the novel, *Blood and Money?*

A Joan Robinson Hill
B Ima Hogg

C Betty Gore
D Lonita Makinson

465 Besides inventing things, Gail Borden helped his brother lay out what town?
A Columbus
B Wharton
C Houston
D Addison

466 Where did sportswriting legends Blackie Sherrod, Bud Shrake, Gary Cartwright and Dan Jenkins work on the same staff?
A *The Dallas Morning News*
B *The Austin American Statesman*
C *The Fort Worth Press*
D *The San Antonio Light*

467 Who won the first ever chili cookoff in Terlingua?
A H. Allen Smith
B Wick Fowler
C Wick Fowler and H. Allen Smith in a draw
D David Witts

468 What successful Broadway choreographer hails from Wichita Falls?
A John Tower
B Tommy Tune
C Ben Vereen
D Lloyd Ruby

469 Ace Reid is a legendary Texas ________.

A Millionaire cattle baron
B Jail breaker
C Cartoonist
D Beer chugging champion

470 Who discovered the East Texas oil field in 1930?

A Sid Richardson
B Joe Exxon
C H.L. Hunt
D C.M. "Dad" Joiner

471 Who was a founder of Muse Air?

A Herb Kelleher
B Lamar Muse
C Rollin King
D Howard Putnam

472 Identify Midland Minnie.

A A local bag lady who hangs out at the Bar
B Mascot of the Midland Cubs
C Part of a 20,000 year old skull found near Midland
D Legendary West Texas female truck driver

473 What Houston TV reporter is credited — or blamed — for the closing of La Grange's Chicken Ranch?

A Chip Moody
B Ron Stone

C Marvin Zindler
D John Lander

474 About half of the Lake Mineral Wells State Park used to be part of what U.S. Army Post?
A Fort Phantom Hill
B Fort Worth
C Camp Bowie
D Fort Wolters

475 Who succeeded Preston Smith as governor of Texas?
A John Hill
B Dolph Briscoe
C Mark White
D John Connally

476 What did Augustus and John K. Allen develop?
A Polio vaccine
B Radar detectors
C Southwest Conference recruiting standards
D Houston

477 One of the largest shrimp fleets in the world is based at which Texas port?
A Levelland
B Brownsville
C Galveston
D Port Worth

478 What was the most important city in Northeast Texas in 1860?

A Dallas
B Jefferson
C Texarkana
D Athens

479 What Texas State Park moves?
A Texas State Railway
B San Jacinto Monument
C Palo Duro State Park
D Big Thicket

480 How wide is Texas?
A 773 miles
B Miles and miles and miles
C 500,000,000,000 feet
D 1,000 miles

481 Who made "San Antonio Rose" famous?
A George "The Ice Man" Gervin
B Pancho Villa
C Bob Wills
D Tanya Tucker

482 Who became world famous as J.R. Ewing on the television series, "Dallas"?
A Patrick Duffy
B Finlay Ewing
C J.R. Duncan
D Larry Hagman

483 The very spot where Don Juan de Onate founded El Paso del Norte in 1598 is now part of what city?

A El Paso
B Juarez
C Presidio
D Albuquerque

484 What major lake is near Graham, Texas?
A Lake 'o the Pines
B Inks Lake
C Lake Limestone
D Possum Kingdom

485 Name the top tourist city in Texas.
A Dallas
B Corpus Christi
C Houston
D San Antonio

486 Although Ada Price and Dolphin Floyd never knew each other, what Texas town was named for the both of them?
A Adelphia
B Dolphinada
C Afp
D Floydada

487 Who was the first manager of the Texas Rangers baseball club?
A Ted Williams
B Billy Martin
C Whitey Herzog
D Bobby Valentine

488 Galveston's Ashton Villa was one of the first homes west of the Mississippi

to be constructed of what?
A Brick
B Adobe
C Aluminum used in mobile homes
D Solid steel

Where is the Internal Revenue Service located in Texas?
A River Oaks
B Austin
C Midland
D Happy

When Texans mixed three-eighths Brahman and five-eighths shorthorn, what did they get?
A A midget rodeo bull
B Santa Gertrudis
C Two confused bulls
D Charolais

Which of the following were born in Panola County, Texas?
A Jim Reeves
B Geraldine Ferraro
C Tex Ritter
D David Ritter

In what 1982 movie do Terry Jastrow and Anne Archer play a couple of wildcatters looking for oil in Texas?
A "Back to the Future"
B "Giant"
C "Waltz Across Texas"

D "Looking for Oil in all the Wrong Places"

493 What is the official name for the Port of Houston?

A The Port of Houston

B Harris County Authority Canal and Seaport

C Astroport

D Gulf of Mexico Ship Channel Seaport at Houston

494 Where did the Texans defeat Santa Anna?

A The Alamo

B Goliad

C Gonzales

D San Jacinto

495 Who visited Langtry, Texas after Judge Roy Bean died?

A President Teddy Roosevelt

B John Wayne

C Lillie Langtry

D The New Law West of the Pecos

496 What was unique about George C. Childress signing the Texas Declaration of Independence?

A He forgot his pen

B He wasn't supposed to sign it

C He was against independence

D He wrote the document

497 Bill Moyers was press secretary to what U.S. President?

A Dwight Eisenhower
B John Kennedy
C Lyndon Johnson
D Ronald Reagan

What is the state stone?
A Granite
B Diamond
C Palmwood
D Sly and the Family

What world championship is held in Muleshoe, Texas?
A Muleshoe pitching
B Quiche cookoff
C Cattledrive bean cooking for cowboys
D Hang gliding

500 What do the red, white and blue in the Texas flag stand for?
A Blood, sweat and tears
B Stars and stripes forever
C Courage, purity and loyalty
D Insider trading, innocence and wealth

501 Who was the first man executed in Texas after the reinstatement of the death penalty?
A Charlie Brooks, Jr.
B Elmer Wayne Henley
C John Wesley Hardin
D Billy the Kid

502 Who was voted the MVP in the SWC basketball race in 1985?

A Jon Koncak, SMU
B Alvin Franklin, Houston
C Bubba Jennings, Tech
D Dennis Nutt, TCU

503 Texas was under what flag from 1519-1685?

A France
B Confederacy
C Mexico
D Spain

504 Where was the first oil well in Texas drilled?

A North Dallas
B Kilgore
C Ranger
D Nacogdoches

505 Who was the first woman to be licensed as a chauffeur in Texas?

A Jan Korkames
B Jane Wolfe
C Debbie Wagner
D Farrah Fawcett

506 What was the name of the Benedict ranch in "Giant"?

A Catarina
B Reata
C The Four Sixes
D El Rancho de Hatley

507 What two Texans served as National Chairmen of the Democratic Party during the 1970's?

A Mark White
B Robert Strauss
C John White
D Kent Hance

508 Who is Houston's celebrated television doctor?

A Dr. Red Duke
B Dr. Larry Arnspiger
C Dr. Lawrence Oliver
D Dr. Chip Moody

509 What happened on March 2, 1836?

A Texas became the 28th state to be admitted to the union
B Santa Anna's forces overtook the Alamo, killing all Texans
C The Texas Declaration of Independence was signed
D Doak Walker won the Heisman Trophy

510 While the Shah of Iran's son was going through flight training at Reece Air Force Base, in which Texas city did he choose to live?

A Temple
B Lubbock
C Houston
D Kerrville

511 Duncan Reynaldo became famous as whom?
A Freddie Fender
B Governor Mark White
C John Denver
D The Cisco Kid

512 Where was Texas rock singer Janis Joplin found dead?
A Hollywood (Landmark Hotel)
B Dallas (Tower Motel)
C Port Arthur (Holiday Inn)
D Lubbock (Red Raider Inn)

513 What major company did Bette Graham start?
A Graham Cracker Co.
B First National Bank in Graham
C Liquid Paper
D MTV

514 Who were the members of "Phi Slama Jama"?
A The cast from the movie "Animal House"
B The University of Houston Cougar basketball team
C The SAE's at Texas Tech
D Those who went through Harlem Globetrotter rush

515 Name the Texas sprinter who won three gold medals in the '56 Olympics.
A Carl Lewis
B Bobby Morrow

C Will Francis
D Johnny “Lam” Jones

516 Who was the 5′3″ quarterback for the 1967 SMU Mustangs?
A Inez Perez
B Eddie LeBaron
C Don McIlhenney
D Keith Bobo

517 Name the first Texas woman to be appointed a federal judge.
A Sarah T. Hughes
B Linda Thomas
C Frances Farenthold
D Martha McKenzie

518 Who is the only athlete in Southwest Conference football history to be named All-SWC three years in a row, at three different positions?
A “Super Bill” Bradley, Texas
B Wayne Morris, SMU
C Tommy Nobis, Texas
D Gary Hammond, SMU

519 For whom was Lubbock, Texas named?
A Governor Frank R. Lubbock
B Col. Tom Lubbock, organizer of Terry’s Texas Rangers
C Early settler Matt Malouf Lubbock
D Famous Indian Chief “Running Deer” Lubbock

520 What is the name of the huge trade days in Canton, Texas?

A First Monday
B Van Zandt County Fair
C Canton Weekly Garage Sale and Chili cook-off
D "Huge Trade Days"

521 Name the two actresses who were nominated for an Oscar for their performances in "Terms of Endearment."

A Debra Winger
B Shirley MacLaine
C Cher
D Lelise Folse

522 "It's So Easy" is a song written by whom?

A Roger Staubach
B Craig Hall
C Buddy Holly
D Rusty Weir

523 Who wrote, *Blood Will Tell,* the book based on the Cullen Davis trial?

A James Michener
B Cullen Davis
C Gary Cartwright
D Thomas Thompson

524 Where in Texas is Schlitz beer brewed?

A Longview
B San Antonio

C Houston
D Luckenbach

525 What is the year of Texas' Sesquicentennial Celebration?
A 1836
B 1936
C 1986
D 2036

526 What limousine service, featuring white Cadillac convertibles with steer horns, premiered in Dallas in 1981?
A Cowboy Cadillacs, Inc.
B Billy Bob's Shuttle Service
C Texas Taxi
D Ragtop Rides of Dallas

527 Houston's Convention Center was named for which former congressman?
A Louie Welch
B Albert Thomas
C Barbara Jordan
D Dan Pastorini

528 Who donated the land for the first state park in Texas?
A The dinosaurs
B Governor Pat Neff's mother
C Lady Bird Johnson
D Jim Bowie

529 What is the Kilgore Junior College drill team called?
A Apache Bells

B Rangerettes
C Dancin' Kilgirls
D Doomsday Defense

530 What state leads the nation in the sales of pick-up trucks?
A Texas
B Texas
C Texas
D Texas

531 What is the name of John Connally's ranch near Floresville?
A Connally Acres
B Floresville Farm
C Picosa
D Lazy S

532 What is the name of the Amtrak train which runs through Temple and Texarkana?
A *Silver Streak*
B *Battleship Texas*
C *Texas Zephyr*
D *The Eagle*

533 What U.S. President went to the Big Shootout, the 1969 football match between Texas and Arkansas for the national championship?
A Ronald Reagan
B Jimmy Carter
C Gerald Ford
D Richard "Hook 'em Horns" Nixon

534 What other states in the union were independent republics?

A Arizona
B Oklahoma
C California
D None

535 What was Dwight Eisenhower's nickname?

A "Bum"
B "Ike"
C "Froggie"
D "Geek"

536 What happened to Texas gunfighter William P. Longley?

A He rode off into the sunset
B He moved to Hollywood and bought the California Angels
C He was hanged in 1877
D He ran for governor and beat John Hill

537 What are you if you are a Dallas Harlequin?

A A comedian from North Texas
B A rugby player
C You are on parole for a misdemeanor
D Reader of novels

538 Who was Texas' most famous pirate?

A Roberto Clemente
B Long John Silver

C Billie Sol Estes
D Jean Lafitte

539 What was Tex Ritter's real name?
A Woodward Maurice Ritter
B Rutherford Ritter III
C John Boy Ritter
D Texas A. Ritter

540 Name the only all-Texas professional football title game ever.
A 1962 Houston Oilers vs Dallas Texans (AFL)
B 1975 Dallas Cowboys vs Houston Oilers (NFL)
C 1984 San Antonio Gunslingers vs Houston Gamblers (USFL)
D 1985 SMU Mustangs vs TCU Horned Frogs (NCAA)

541 Who is the all-time Texas high school career leader in rushing?
A John David Crow
B Curtis Dickey
C Tommy Ferguson
D Ken Hall

542 One can find an indoor rodeo at ____________.
A Carl's Truck Stop
B Billy Bob's Texas
C Walt Garrison's house
D Love Field

543 In terms of population, what is the second largest town in Dallas County?

A Dallas
B Garland
C Plano
D Richardson

544 What town got its name from the W.E. Stewart Land Company?

A Stewartsville
B Weslaco
C Levelland
D West

545 What town was *not* served by the *Sam Houston Zephyr,* the state's first streamlined passenger train?

A Houston
B Dallas
C Fort Worth
D Marfa

546 Led by Rick Bullock, what team won the first SWC post-season basketball tournament?

A Houston Cougars
B Texas Tech Red Raiders
C SMU Mustangs
D Arkansas Razorbacks

547 Name the first black quarterback in the SWC to lead his team to the Cotton Bowl Classic.

A Jerry Levias of SMU
B Earl Campbell of Texas

C Kevin Murray of Texas A&M
D Danny Davis of Houston

548 What Texas singer/songwriter wrote and recorded a song called "Wildfire"?
A Billy Gibbons
B Michael Murphey
C Shake Russell
D Willie Nelson

549 Who was known as the original "Singing Cowboy"?
A Don Meredith ("Turn out the Lights . . .")
B Lance Rentzel
C Gene Autry
D Hoss Cartwright

550 Who was the star of Fort Worth-produced Slam Bang Theater?
A Icky Twerp
B Mr. Peppermint
C Officer Friendly
D Eddie Chiles

551 In the song, "London Homesick Blues," by Gary P. Nunn, where was the rendezvous with the English girl?
A Big Ben
B Charles and Di's place
C On the third floor
D Armadillo World Headquarters

552 What famous rocker from Wink, Texas, sang "Only the Lonely"?

A Roy Orbison
B Waylon Jennings
C Jay Boy Adams
D Stevie Ray Vaughan

553 Who was the youngest governor of Texas?
A Benny Carpenter (35)
B Dan Moody (34)
C Kent Hance (40)
D John Connally (37)

554 The Frio and Atascosa Rivers are tributaries of what river?
A The Nile
B The Brazos
C The Nueces
D The Thames

555 What did Governor Sam Houston do when Texas seceeded?
A Fainted
B Went fishing
C Enlisted
D Resigned

556 The Texas Prison Rodeo is held on what day of the week each October?
A Sunday
B Monday
C Friday
D Saturday

557 The original source of the Red River is in what state?

A Texas
B Oklahoma
C New Mexico
D Colorado

558 Who was the first Republican governor of Texas?
A William P. Clements
B Edmund J. Davis
C James M. Moroney III
D Davy Crockett

559 What caused Jack Ruby's death?
A Lethal injection
B Suicide
C A single shot fired by Lee Harvey Oswald
D Cancer

560 What physical feature is the boundary between Texas and Arkansas for 40 miles?
A A barbed wire fence
B Sabine River
C Red River
D Bigfoot's footprint

561 What Texas corporation built the bicycle velodrome for the 1984 Summer Olympics in Los Angeles?
A Shell Oil Company
B The Southland Corporation
C Texas Instruments
D Elms Faris and Co.

562 What football coach at St. Mary's in San Antonio went on to become the President of the United States?

A Lyndon B. Johnson
B George Washington
C Dwight Eisenhower
D George Bush

563 What does Cinco de Mayo celebrate?

A Mexico's defeat of France at Puebla in 1862
B The glorious loss at San Jacinto to the Texas rebels
C The victory of the Alamo
D Mexican Independence from Spain

564 Who became known as "Slingin' Sammy"?

A Sammy Baugh (TCU quarterback)
B Sammy Davis, Jr. (entertainer)
C Sammy Papert (New Westexico newspaper ad salesman)
D Sam Snead (golfer)

565 Name the owner of the Texas Rangers before Eddie Chiles bought in.

A Ted Williams
B Cullen Davis
C The Bass Brothers
D Brad Corbett

566 What star of "Deep Throat" was born in Bryan, Texas, in 1949?

A Linda Lovelace
B Harry Reems

C John Holmes
D Cathy Rigby

567 Who wrote the best-seller, *Semi Tough?*
A Peter Gent
B Dan Jenkins
C Craig Morton
D Joe Bob Briggs

568 Where is the annual Tornado Jam held in Texas?
A Memorial Stadium in Austin
B Lubbock
C The Cotton Bowl in Dallas
D Wichita Falls

569 Who wrote the song, "Crazy"?
A Patsy Cline
B Waylon Jennings
C Michael Murphey
D Willie Nelson

570 Who played the role of the deputy in the movie version of "The Best Little Whorehouse in Texas"?
A Jim Nabors
B Burt Reynolds
C Dom Deluise
D Larry L. King

571 When was the Luckenbach Dance Hall built?
A 1880
B 1496

C 1986
D 1900

572 Who speaks the following languages: Ido, Ibo, Hausa and Yoruba?
A Henry Kissinger
B Lt. Governor Bill Hobby
C Kareem Olajuwon
D Eben Price

573 What is the name of the Rice mascot?
A Hooter
B Hoo-Hoo
C Sammy
D Chumley

574 Known as "Mr. Southwest Conference," which radio sports announcer brought SWC football to life for the Humble Football Network?
A Kern Tips
B Jack Dale
C Brad Sham
D Gene Elston

575 Who played the role of Sissy in "Urban Cowboy"?
A John Travolta
B Debra Winger
C Mary Anna Austin
D Morgan Fairchild

576 What North Texas duo was known for their song, "Summer Breeze"?
A Stevens and Pruitt
B Seals and Crofts

C Thayer and Harris
D Wacker and Lowe

577 Who played the lead in the Texas-filmed "Great Waldo Pepper"?
A Robert Redford
B Paul Newman
C Waldo Pepper
D King Charlie Hillard

578 Who won the NCAA basketball championship in Houston in 1971?
A University of Houston
B Western Kentucky
C UCLA
D Villanova

579 What kicker holds the record for the longest Dallas Cowboy field goal?
A Raphael Septian
B Tony Fritsch
C Colin Ridgeway
D Brian Hall

580 Where did the Texas Longhorns play basketball before moving into the "Super Drum"?
A Gregory Gym
B Daniel Meyers Coliseum
C Heart 'o Texas Coliseum
D Memorial Stadium

581 What kind of beer was being transported in "Smokey and the Bandit"?
A Lone Star

B Coors
C Billy Beer
D Pearl Light

What El Paso native is a former wife of Eddie Fisher?
A Babs Greyhosky
B Debbie Reynolds
C Tina Turner
D Bad News Barnes

583 What color is *not* in the Texas flag?
A Lavender
B Red
C White
D Blue

584 What is Mimus Polyglottos?
A Another former wife of Eddie Fisher
B A large bass found in East Texas bayous
C Mockingbird
D A Texas disease caused by overeating jalepenos

585 Where did Walter Cronkite go to high school?
A L.D. Bell in Hurst
B Midland Lee
C Tyler John Tyler
D Houston San Jacinto

586 What Texas city has a hospital called Parkland?
A Parkland, Texas

B McAllen
C Galveston
D Dallas

587 What is Texas' principle commercial timber?
A Pine
B Cedar
C Oak
D Mahogany

588 What is the destination of the El Paso aerial tramway?
A Mexico
B New Mexico
C Ranger Peak
D Happy Hour at the State Line Restaurant

589 What are upon you till Gabriel blows his horn?
A The Eyes of Texas
B Fire ants
C A couple of Gabriel's doberman pinschers
D Your guardian angels

590 What other person besides President Kennedy was shot in the tragic motorcade in Dallas in 1963?
A Jack Ruby
B Governor John Connally
C Kennedy's chauffeur
D Vice-President Johnson

591 What is the interstate highway connecting Dallas and Houston?
A I-35
B I-45
C I-10
D I-20

592 What monument stands in front of the city hall at Poteet, Texas?
A A seven-foot strawberry
B A replica of the San Jacinto Monument
C A statue of Little Poteet
D A ten-foot statue of Willie Nelson

593 What was opened on May 16, 1888?
A The dance hall in Gruene
B The Capitol Building in Austin
C The Oklahoma border
D *The Dallas Morning News*

594 Who is the founder of *Texas Monthly?*
A J. Frank Dobie
B Don Graham
C Wick Allison
D Michael Levy

595 Name the official bird of The Texas Centennial Exposition.
A Whooping Crane
B Roadrunner
C Owl
D Mockingbird

596 Where in Texas does a statue of a white deer stand in the middle of a

downtown intersection?
A White Deer
B Weatherford
C Midland
D Fredericksburg

597 Which two of the following flags have flown over Texas twice?
A Confederacy
B United States
C Texas
D Mexico

598 What is the largest chain of Mexican restaurants in America?
A On the Border
B El Chico
C El Fenix
D Prufrocko

599 Where is Huston-Tillotson College?
A Austin
B Georgetown
C Houston
D McKinney

600 What is the second largest city in Texas?
A Dallas
B Houston
C Fort Worth
D Bug Tussle

601 You take Ranch Road 1 to get to ________.

A The Twilight Zone
B The LBJ Ranch
C Heaven
D The King Ranch

602 Where is Howard Payne College?
A Brownwood
B Howard
C El Paso
D There's no such thing

603 Who is TCU's all-time basketball scoring leader?
A Eugene "Goo" Kennedy
B Dennis Nutt
C Darrell Browder
D Chuck Rosebrough

604 Who was "Captain Crash," the Cowboys' hard-hitting defensive back?
A Charlie Waters
B Bill Bates
C Cliff Harris
D Mel Renfro

605 What is the southernmost town in Texas?
A Perryton
B Cancun
C Laredo
D Brownsville

606 How many delegates did John Connally win during the 1980 Republican Presidential primary?

A 159
B 177
C 206
D 1

607 What intrastate airline connected Dallas Love Field with Houston Hobby and changed the way thousands of Texans travel?
A Southwest Airlines
B People Express
C Braniff International
D Amtrak

What does a cowboy wear to protect his legs from scratches?
A Bikini underwear
B Hand lotion
C Chaps
D Shoulder pads

609 The Daughters of the Republic of Texas would not allow what movie to be filmed at the Alamo?
A "The Alamo"
B "Viva Max!"
C "The Daughters Do Dallas"
D "South Pacific"

610 Who was the first black star receiver in SWC football?
A Charley Pride, Ole Miss
B Larry Dupre, Texas Tech
C Jerry Levias, SMU
D Terry Dorsey, Imatellin U

611 What is the name of the ancient oil rig located on the UT-Austin campus?

A Old Ironsides
B Austin McCloud #2
C Santa Rita #1
D Spindletop

612 Comanche Chief Quanah Parker had a brother named ________.

A Bubba
B QP2
C Ensign Parker
D Pecos

613 What was Lyndon Johnson's middle name?

A Billy Bob
B Baines
C Fitzgerald
D Benjamin

614 What does Val Verde mean?

A Green Valley
B "Where is the restroom?"
C "How's it goin', Val?"
D "Forget the Alamo!"

615 When did Hoss die?

A Actor Dan Blocker died in 1972
B When "Bonanza" was cancelled
C He's alive and living in Argentina
D 1959

616 Madalyn Murray O'Hair is a legendary Texas ________.

A Nun
B Astronaut
C Rodeo queen
D Atheist

617 Who should be credited with the line, "The night life ain't no good life, but it's my life"?
A Dan Pastorini
B Lance Rentzel
C Willie Nelson
D Don Meredith

618 Where did Boz Scaggs and Steve Miller attend high school together?
A Allen Academy, San Marcos
B St. Mark's, Dallas
C Estacado, Lubbock
D R.L. Turner, Carrollton

619 Texan Jack Boles played whose Confederate father in "The Littlest Rebel"?
A Brooke Shields
B Kathy Whitmire
C Shirley Temple
D Vivian Leigh

620 When does Texas okra thrive?
A During the hot season
B During the ski season
C There is no okra in Texas
D When it's fried and eaten

621 What was the second flag to fly over Texas?

A Spain
B France
C United States
D Texas

622 What was Granite Shoals Lake renamed as?
A Granite Shoals Pond
B Lake Limestone
C Johnson Lake
D Granite Shores Lake

623 Who is considered "the father of Texas Archaeology"?
A Lamar Muse
B Stephen F. Austin
C Dr. J.E. Pearce
D Dr. Frank N. Furter

624 What Texas fort was the first permanent army air base?
A Fort Worth
B Fort Sam Houston
C Fort Griffin
D Fort Intercontinental

625 Who mailed his first letter in Hye, Texas?
A H. Ross Perot
B Nobody in Hye has ever mailed a letter
C Lyndon Johnson
D Larry McMurtry

626 What was unusual about Jose Antonio Navarro's brothers' names?

A They were all misspelled on purpose
B He had no brothers
C They were all named Jose
D They were called Mary, Lisa and Clarita

627 Name the first Texas Tech basketball player to play in the NBA.
A Geoff Huston
B Don Moore
C Blake Taylor
D Keith Kitchens

628 Why was the second game of a double-header in Midland called off on August 7, 1972?
A A tornado was coming out of right field
B Nobody paid the light bill
C Thousands of grasshoppers swarmed the field
D Everyone went to the Bennigan's grand opening

629 Who was the first Houston Rocket to win the NBA MVP award?
A Calvin Murphy
B Moses Malone
C Ralph Sampson
D Akeem Olajuwon

630 Who was the most famous member of the "Sons of the Pioneers"?
A Roy Rogers
B Stephen F. Austin

C Bond Beams
D Charles Goodnight

631 What Houston pop singer is known for his hit, "I Can See Clearly Now"?
A Johnny Nash
B Meatloaf
C Billy Gibbons
D Archie Bell

632 Fort Mason was the site of whose last command in the U.S. Army?
A Sgt. Barry Sadler
B Colonel Clink
C Gen. Robert E. Lee
D Gen. Douglas MacArthur

633 For its size, what is the most dangerous snake in Texas?
A Milk snake
B Ribbon snake
C Coral snake
D Hill Country earthworm

634 What plant has the most species in Texas?
A Nuclear plant
B Cactus
C Mesquite
D Cotton

Girls Industrial College, opened in 1903, is now called what?
A The University of Texas at Austin
B Lewisville High School

C Rice
D Texas Women's University

636 The Texas and Pacific Railroad was absorbed by whom?
A Amtrak
B Missouri and Pacific
C Craig Hall
D Lionel

637 Where is the Texas Medical Center?
A Houston
B Galveston
C Dallas
D San Antonio

638 In the late 70's, the largest solar collector in the world was located in what West Texas town?
A Alpine
B Crosbyton
C Atlanta
D Wheeler

639 Where was the Fire Museum of Texas built?
A Grand Prairie
B Red Adair's den
C Georgetown
D Paris, Texas

640 What observatory is located at Fort Davis?
A McDonald Observatory
B Jack-in-the-Box Observatory

C Fort Stockton Observatory
D Casa Manana

641 When Houston beat Tulsa in football 100-6 in 1968, who scored the Cougars' 92nd point?
A Elvin Hayes
B Willie Nelson
C Oral Roberts
D Larry Gatlin

642 What Dallas Cowboy quarterback went on to be a pro football head coach?
A Eddie LeBaron
B Craig Morton
C Don Meredith
D John Roach

643 What famous jockey was born in Fabens, Texas?
A Tina Caperton
B Billy Shoemaker
C Sam Baldwin
D Philip Wildman

644 In the movie, "Terms of Endearment," what was Jack Nicholson's occupation?
A Psychiatrist
B Astronaut
C Term life insurance salesman
D Border patrol guard

645 Where is the world-famous Amon Carter Museum?
A Fort Worth
B Canyon

C Arlington
D Huntsville

Who made the hit out of Michael Murphey's song, “Cherokee Fiddle”?

A Quanah Parker
B Gary P. Nunn
C Prince
D Johnny Lee

Who played the role of sweet Jacy in “The Last Picture Show”?

A Cybill Shephard
B Cloris Leachman
C Ben Johnson
D Allison Foster

When Paul Newman played “Harry,” who played his “Son”?

A Robert Redford
B Robby Benson
C Tony Dorsett
D Tommy Tune

Where did world-class tennis stars Cliff Richey, Anne Smith, Dick Stockton and Bill Scanlon attend college?

A Stanford
B UCLA
C Trinity
D Hardin Simmons

650 What word has *not* been on a Texas license plate:

A Sesquicentennial
B Centennial

C Hemisfair
D Oklahoma

651 Who was the Dallas Maverick's first draft pick ever? (Hint: He never played for the Mavericks).
A Herschel Walker
B Kiki Vandeweghe
C Spud Webb
D World Free

652 What is Farrah Fawcett's real name?
A Farrah Fawcett
B Ellen Hoffman
C Charlotte Dyer
D Catherine Bowe

653 Name the town in Texas founded by the originator of Post Toasties.
A Battle Creek
B Post
C Waco
D Cisco

654 What is Texas' longest tunnel?
A The Cave at Six Flags Over Texas
B The I-30 Tunnel
C The Baytown Tunnel
D The Tunnel of Love

655 The Rice Hotel was where in Houston?
A Where the Galleria is now
B On the site of the old Texas Republic Capitol
C Rice University

D Near the scenic Rice Paddies south of Houston

656 Where is the Texas Ranger Hall of Fame?
A Waco
B Arlington
C New York
D Austin

657 Where can one find the world's largest collection of works by Robert Browning and Elizabeth Barrett?
A Baylor University
B Union 76 Truckstop on I-30 at Rockwall
C Corpus Christi
D London, England

658 What PBS journalist took a walk through the 20th Century, by way of his hometown of Marshall, Texas?
A Jim Lehrer
B Albert Agnor
C Bill Moyers
D Bob Ray Sanders

659 What do you put around the edge of a margarita glass?
A Lysol
B Salt
C Sugar
D Picante

What fish, native to the Nile, has turned up in Texas rivers?

A Catfish
B Sturgeon
C Tilapia
D Alligator gar

What is the Mission San Antonio de Valero?

A Top disco in San Antonio
B The Alamo
C A new country dance step
D Bo Derek's favorite song

Who sang "Take Me Back to Tulsa"?

A Bob Wills
B Jim Moroney
C Phil Keller
D Don Wiviot

663

What did Lorenzo Charles do to Houston in 1983?

A Caused a city-wide garbage collector strike
B Took Howard Hughes' inheritance from the city
C His basket beat the Cougars for the NCAA basketball crown
D Didn't pay all of his city taxes

Who designed the Dallas Theater Center?

A Frank Lloyd Wright
B Paul Baker

C Tom Schutz
D Bea Handel

665 Elisabet Ney was a gifted Texas __________.
A Beer chugging champion
B Sculptor
C *Playboy* centerfold
D Poet

What is the most exclusive section of Houston?
A Fourth Ward
B Meyerland
C Heights
D River Oaks

What Dallas lawyer took an active role in defending both Cullen Davis and Jack Ruby?
A Bert Shipp
B Phil Burleson
C Richard "Racehorse" Haynes
D Steve Norris

668 What is the name of the brewery in Shiner, Texas?
A Spoetzl
B Shiner
C Chudej Bros.
D Strunk Bros. Land & Cattle Co. and Brewery

Herman Lay of Dallas headed what business conglomerate?

A Texaco
B Frito-Lay
C Shiner Beer
D Lincoln Property Co.

670 What state leads the nation in oil and natural gas production?
A New Mexico
B Rhode Island
C Texas
D California

671 What did Patsy McClenny of Dallas change her name to?
A Patsy Ann McClenny
B Racquel Welch
C Bubbles Cash
D Morgan Fairchild

672 Who sang about "goin' back to Houston . . ."?
A Dean Martin
B Jerry Lewis
C Louie Welch
D Neill Armstrong

673 Who wrote the theme song for the television series, "Dallas"?
A Ron Chapman
B Floyd Cramer
C Johnny Knight
D Henry Mancini

674 What Texas native played the title role in "The Amazing Mr. Hughes"?
A Tommy Lee Jones

B Powers Booth
C Lott McIlhenney
D Jerry Haynes

675 Where was singer Jim Croce going when his plane crashed?
A Florida Keys
B Clear Lake, Iowa
C Sherman, Texas
D Nashville, Tennessee

676 What Texas city was the title of a 1969 Glen Campbell hit song?
A "Abilene"
B "Galveston"
C "Houston"
D "El Paso"

677 Who's resignation from the U.S. Senate in 1960 caused the need for a special election in Texas in 1961?
A Sam Rayburn
B Gary Galbraith
C John Tower
D Lyndon Johnson

678 Why did the University of Texas originally have no president?
A They couldn't find anyone qualified
B The University of Virginia didn't have one
C The governor ran the school
D Darrell Royal wasn't born yet

679 How long did Old Rip, the horned toad, live in the Eastland County courthouse cornerstone?

A Two hours
B Two days
C 10 weeks
D 31 years

What is the most popular garden vegetable in Texas?

A Marijuana
B Cactus
C Tomato
D Okra

Name the third largest city in Texas.

A Houston
B San Antonio
C Fort Worth
D Austin

What is the largest river between the Red and Rio Grande rivers?

A Brazos
B Pecos
C Colorado
D Trinity

Name the Texas A&M quarterback who twice made All-Southwest Conference in the 70's then ran for Congress in 1985.

A Kevin Murray
B Edd Hargett
C Jim Hilscher
D Tom Wilson

684 Who is the Dallas Maverick General Manager who was the man most responsible for bringing the NBA to Dallas?

A Billy Martin
B Hal Browning
C Don Carter
D Norm Sonju

685 Who was the first Texan to win a gold medal in Olympic track competition?

A Carl Lewis
B Billy Mills
C Charles Paddock
D Betty Crocker

686 What former Texas Tech coach had a namesake son on the PGA Tour?

A Lee Trevino
B Payne Stewart
C DeWitt Weaver
D Steve Sloan

687 What was the name of the major motion picture theater chain in Texas from the mid-30's to the late 60's?

A Interstate Theaters
B Loew's Anatole
C Trans-Texas
D Texas Chainsaw Theaters

688 How many people died in the plane crash which killed Buddy Holly?

A One
B Four

C 55
D 179

What San Antonio actress married Richard Benjamin?
A Paula Prentiss
B Carol Burnett
C Cynthia Taylor
D Chelsea Dodgen

What Nacogdoches street is believed to be the oldest street in America?
A Westheimer
B Lovers Lane
C North Street
D Martin Luther King Dr.

Who murdered the French explorer Rene Robert Cavelier Sieur de la Salle in Grimes County in 1687?
A Bigfoot
B Henry Lee Lucas
C One of his own men
D Santa Anna

What did the Sanger Brothers install in their store in Dallas in 1909 that was a first?
A Cash registers
B Underground parking
C Television monitors
D Escalators

What Texas building has been billed as "The Eighth Wonder of the World"?

A Reunion Tower, Dallas
B Astrodome, Houston
C State Capitol, Austin
D Casa Manana, Fort Worth

Where was Lyndon Johnson sworn in as President?
A Aboard *Air Force One* at Love Field in Dallas
B Washington, D.C.
C LBJ Ranch
D Joe Miller's, Dallas

695 Identify Leon McAuliffe.
A First graduate of Texas A&M
B Bob Wills' steel guitarist
C Heisman Trophy winner from TCU
D The only coach the Dallas Cowboys have ever known

Who designed the Stetson hat?
A John B. Stetson
B George Strait
C Mike Hatley
D Dee Wickson

697 What was Mary Martin's childhood hometown?
A Plainview
B Terrell
C Weatherford
D Dallas

What did J. Frank Dobie name his ranch?

A King Ranch
B Paisano
C Dobie Brothers Farm
D Fred Acres

699 Who flew the *Winnie Mae?*
A Howard Hughes
B Howard Putnam
C Howard Cosell
D Wiley Post

700 What Texas developer is known for building the Galleria?
A Gerald Hines
B Trammell Crow
C Harold Farb
D Mack Pogue

701 What is George Bush's favorite place to jog in Houston?
A Southwest Freeway
B Downtown
C River Oaks
D Memorial Park

702 Who was Priscilla Davis' Fort Worth lover who was murdered at Cullen Davis' mansion?
A Sean Lanham
B Delbert McClinton
C Stan Farr
D Richard "Racehorse" Haynes

703 When did Texas' legendary "imagineer" Hondo Crouch die?

A 1964
B 1972
C 1976
D 1980

704 What Texan co-produced the hit movie "Terms of Endearment"?
A Ross Milloy
B Martin Jurrow
C Horton Foote
D Sam Grogg

705 What is Fort Worth's Sid Bass' middle name?
A Large-mouth
B Richardson
C Rutherford
D Harry

706 What is the work of art along I-40 west of Amarillo in which several Cadillacs are buried halfway in the ground (fins up)?
A Larry Lange Ranch
B Cristo's Caddies
C Cadillac Ranch
D Palo Duro Pile-up

707 Chadium Diamond Manufacturing of Belgium applied for a patent on what Texas item?
A Barbed wire
B Chili
C Diamonds cut in the shape of Texas
D Weed Eater

708 How many shots were fired at Bonnie and Clyde when they were killed?
A Two
B Ten
C 34
D Over 200

709 What Texas writer wrote *A Woman of Independent Means?*
A Ken Milstead
B Elizabeth Forsythe Hailey
C David Seeley
D Angela Enright

710 Who put out the bumper sticker, "_________ and Longnecks, No Place but Texas"?
A Lone Star Beer
B Texas Tourism Bureau
C Hicks Printing, Garland
D Gilley's Club in Houston

711 Where was the first 7-Eleven?
A Boca Raton, Florida
B Beaver Creek, Colorado
C Edgefield and 12th in Dallas
D Mountain View, California

712 Who was Cactus Jack? (Hint: He was a Vice-President of the U.S.)
A John Nance Garner of Uvalde
B Jack Crozier of Dallas
C Jack Denman of HP
D Jack Wood of Odessa

713 Who played the lead role in the movie about Paul "Bear" Bryant?

A Phil Gramm
B Dudley Moore
C Gary Busey
D Gene Stallings

714 Who was the E-Systems engineer convicted of armed robbery, sentenced to life in prison, then released after *60 Minutes* exposed the case?

A Joe Bob Briggs
B Lenel Geter
C Ed Bradley
D John Hinckley

715 Who shot an Indian from a mile away in the Second Battle of Adobe Walls?

A Davy Crockett
B Jim Bowie
C Billy Dixon
D Hopalong Cassidy

716 What Texas Indian scout got his nickname because of his large feet?

A William "Bigfoot" Wallace
B Bruce "Bigfoot" Jolesch
C "Bignose" Kate of Ft. Griffin
D Ed "Too Tall" Jones

717 What Texas company once promoted "the end of the plain plane"?

A Braniff International
B Muse Air

C Continental Airlines
D Amtrak

718 What singing cowboy made "Back in the Saddle Again" a hit?
A Danny White
B Roy Rogers
C Tom Landry
D Gene Autry

719 What was Governor James Hogg's daughter's name?
A Ura
B Ima
C Porky
D Whata

720 What two Texans owned the Terlingua ranch where the first chili cookoff was held?
A David Witts
B Hoss Cartwright
C Carroll Shelby
D H.L. Hunt

721 Who was "Brother Bill," the disc jockey at the country and western radio station in Lockhart?
A Bill Hitzelberger
B Bill Nelson
C Bill Hailey
D Waylon Jennings

722 Name Dallas' longtime District Attorney who prosecuted Jack Ruby.

A Henry Wade
B Rick "Racehorse" Addison
C Jim Mattox
D Will Fritz

723 In 1976, which SWC kicker was *not* named to any All-American teams?
A Russell Erxleben, Texas
B Steve Little, Arkansas
C Ecomet Burley, Texas Tech
D Tony Franklin, Texas A&M

724 What black athlete broke the color barrier in the SWC in 1966 when he became a Baylor Bear?
A Lee Westbrook
B Jerry Levias
C Earl Campbell
D Kareem Abdul Jabbar

725 What is the most popular country dance?
A The Twist
B The Freddie
C The Two-Step
D The Bump

726 What does Mac Davis want to be wearing when he's buried in Lubbock?
A A Texas Tech cheerleader outfit
B A three-piece suit
C A rented tux
D His jeans

727 The Ranchman Cafe is a popular steakhouse in what small town west of

Denton?

A Amarillo
B Ponder
C Los Angeles
D Decatur

728 The inscription, "A President's hardest task is not to do what is right, but to know what is right," is written where?

A The White House
B LBJ Library
C The men's room at the Seguin Holiday Inn
D H. Ross Perot's desk

729 What did the Rocking Chair Ranche call its cowhands?

A Rustlers
B Outlaws
C Doomsday Defense
D Cow Servants

730 Who jumped 29′ 2.5″?

A Bob Beamon
B Old Rip, the Eastland County Horned Toad
C The first molar transplant in Texas
D Anyone who ever saw Bill Bates coming at him

731 Jack Heifner's most famous play is the award-winning "__________".

A "Vanities"
B "Lone Star"

C "Down an Alley Filled With Cats"
D "The Oldest Living Graduate"

732 What happened to Black Jack Ketchum right after he said, "I'll be in hell before you start breakfast, boys. Let 'er rip!"?

A He ate everyone's breakfast
B He became Texas' first parachute tester
C He won the 15th running of the Indianapolis 500
D He was hanged

733 Where did Tony Dorsett play football in college?

A SMU
B Rice
C Pittsburgh
D Slippery Rock

734 Several years after the Champs had a hit called "Tequila" in 1958, what two band members went on to become stars as a duo?

A Donny Osmond
B Marie Osmond
C Jimmy Seals
D Dash Crofts

735 Who sang, "If lovin' you is wrong, I don't want to be right"?

A Lady Bird Johnson
B Barbara Mandrell

C Ginger Brown
D Janie Fricke

736 In Johnny Cash's "Folsom Prison Blues," where was the train going?
A Bent Tree
B Tulsa
C San Antonio
D On a one way ride to Tupelo, Mississippi

737 What do dancers yell during the "Cotton Eyed Joe"?
A "Get off My Toe!"
B "Bull S____!"
C "Turn off the lights!"
D "Next song, please!"

738 An estimated 200,000 Texans served in which war?
A Mexican-American War
B World War I
C World War II
D Vietnam War

739 What foreign country sends the third most tourists to Texas?
A France
B England
C California
D Canada

740 Which of the following Texas governors did *not* serve three terms?
A Price Daniel
B John Connally

C Allan Shivers
D Dolph Briscoe

741 What was the name of Jack Ruby's nightclub?
A Jack's Burger House
B The Carousel
C The Starck Club
D Ruby's

742 Why does the Texas Tech class ring have a bullfighter on it?
A It symbolizes victory in fighting the bull
B They originally were sent the wrong ones, and never switched back
C The Tech mascot used to be a Matador
D Nobody wanted to pay for a stone for the ring

743 What did UT President William Prather used to remind students?
A "Make your grades, or I'll put a bullfighter on your class ring"
B "Ask not what you can do for your school. . ."
C "You should find something to protest, instead of studying"
D "The eyes of Texas are upon you"

744 Out of 10 Texas legislators indicted during the 1970's how many were convicted of anything?
A Eight

B Seven
C Two
D None

745 What major treaty was signed February 2, 1848?
A The Treaty of Secession
B The Alliance of Colorado County
C The Treaty of Guadalupe Hidalgo
D The San Jacinto Victory Pact

746 What is the state flower?
A Bluebonnet
B Indian Paintbrush
C Daisy
D Yucca

747 What was David Allen Coe served while he was performing at Gilley's in mid-1984?
A 15 tequila shots
B A keg of Lone Star beer
C 2,075 shots of bourbon (one from each member of the audience)
D His divorce papers

748 Who was the first man in Texas to purchase an automobile?
A Davy Crockett
B Sam Rayburn
C E.H.R. Greene
D George Blessie

749 Who invented the patented process for condensing milk?

A Elsie the Cow
B Gail Borden
C Joe C. Thompson
D Albert Einstein

750 Who crossed the Texas Plains in 1541?
A Frank X. Tolbert
B Zola Budd
C Coronado
D Craig Breedlove

751 Who is known as "The Mother of Texas"?
A Lynn Moroney
B Jane Long
C Edith Bunker
D Miriam "Ma" Ferguson

752 What was the Big Bopper's real name?
A J.P. Richardson
B George Bopper
C Mickey Holden
D Henry Otto Strunk

753 Who organized the Flying Tigers in 1941?
A Rollin King
B Claire Chennault
C Merle Haggard
D Wiley Post

754 Where is the LaJet Golf Classic held?
A Beaumont
B Bear Creek at D/FW Airport
C The Woodlands
D Abilene

755 Where did the Dallas Cowboys win two Super Bowl championships?
A Orange Bowl in Miami
B Rose Bowl in Los Angeles
C Houston
D New Orleans

756 Billy Ray Smith led what school to the 1977 AAAA state football title?
A Plano
B Brownwood
C Highland Park
D Odessa Permian

757 What Texas city has five military bases?
A Big Spring
B Killeen
C San Antonio
D El Paso

758 What Texas town is named for Teddy Roosevelt's son?
A Teddyville
B Farmer's Branch
C Kermit
D Roosevelt

759 Where is the Cotton Bowl?
A Houston
B Dallas
C Austin
D Irving

760 What is the mascot of Goose Creek High School?

A Ganders
B Cookers
C Waddlers
D Fighting Geese

761 Who was the only SMU quarterback drafted by the Dallas Cowboys?
A Don Meredith
B Lance McIlhenney
C Keith Bobo
D Mike Livingston

762 Who made the "California Quake" famous?
A Butch Johnson
B Bob Arnold
C Tony Hill
D Mike Renfro

763 Who is Baldemar Huerta?
A Henry Cisneros
B Freddie Fender
C Charley Pride
D Martina Navratilova

764 Where was Barbara Mandrell born?
A Disneyland
B Abbott, Texas
C Saratoga
D Houston

765 Where did Pete Gent play pro ball after he left the Cowboys?
A New York Giants
B San Antonio Spurs

C Green Bay Packers
D Dallas Texans

766 Identify Harold Lloyd Jenkins.
A Freddy Fender
B Conway Twitty
C Ferguson Jenkins
D Mark White

767 What Texas actress played Morticia on "The Addams Family"?
A Joan Prather
B Betty Buckley
C Carolyn Jones
D Alice Addams

768 Who directed the motion picture, "The Last Picture Show"?
A Robert Benton
B Peter Bogdanovich
C Ken Harrison
D Michael Hamilton

769 Over $1,000 has been paid in Luling for the Grand Champion what?
A Bull
B Sheep
C Goat
D Watermelon

770 When John Connally married Idanell Brill, who was the best man?
A Ben Barnes
B Richard Nixon
C Lyndon Johnson
D John Connally

771 Where is the highest golf course in Texas?

A Marfa
B Gleneagles
C Lakeway
D Pharoah Country Club

772 Sideoats Gramma is Texas' official what?

A Oats
B Fraternity
C Grass
D Motto

773 What happened when the City of Corsicana drilled for water?

A They struck oil
B It rained for two months
C They never found any
D They hit salt water

774 What were the names of LBJ's two beagles?

A Gray and White
B Him and Her
C Lynda and Luci
D Riff and Raff

775 Where was Conrad Hilton's first hotel?

A Cisco
B Dallas
C Eastland
D Padre Island

776 Who was the SMU coach after Hayden Fry?

A Sonny Allen
B Kellis White
C Dave Smith
D Grant Teaff

777 Who was the first Texas billionaire vegetarian?
A H.L. Hunt
B H. Ross Perot
C J.R. Ewing
D Charles Goodnight

778 Where in Texas can one find the Mandalay Canal?
A Corpus Christi
B Las Colinas in Irving
C Galveston
D Along Mustang Island

779 What brand of Jeans does Big Tex wear at the Texas State Fair?
A Jordache
B Calvin Klein
C Lee
D Levi

780 Where are the most famous stockyards in Texas?
A Lubbock
B Downtown Austin
C Lajitas
D Fort Worth

781 Over 2/3 of the nation's helium is produced where?

A Texas Panhandle
B Gulf Coast
C Big Bend
D East Texas

782 Which of the following is not a camp in Texas?
A Longhorn
B Mystic
C Kickapoo
D Harris County Jail

783 Identify "The Dodger."
A Lee Ioccoca
B Carroll Shelby
C Roger Staubach
D Bill Bates

784 Where in Texas can one find swimming pigs?
A Aquarena Springs (San Marcos)
B Wet 'N Wild (Arlington)
C South Padre Island
D The Greenhouse

785 Name the biggest beer bust in the state.
A Terlingua Chili Cookoff
B Round-up in Austin
C Wurstfest in New Braunfels
D Old Man's Club at the Easy Way, Dallas

786 Why was Belle Starr regularly thrown in jail in Dallas?
A Avoiding the draft
B Horse rustling

C Public nudity
D Murder One (Book 'er, Danno)

787 What Texas-born singer's trademark is wearing dark sunglasses when he performs (and he's not blind)?
A Willis Alan Ramsey
B Roy Orbison
C Joe Ely
D Waylon Jennings

788 Where was Hondo Crouch born?
A Austin
B Aboard a Greyhound bus near Marfa
C Luckenbach
D Hondo

789 Which Texas college has taken the strongest stand against *Playboy* magazine photographing its coeds?
A Texas A&M
B Texas Women's University
C Rice
D Baylor

790 What was the first cattle brand in Texas?
A Lazy-S
B 6666
C AR
D XIT

791 Why was Tyler's Jo-Carroll Dennison well-known in 1942?
A She took off her clothes and rode a

horse through Waco

B She bought a town near Sherman and named it after herself

C She was Miss America

D She was the first woman to hyphenate her name

What U.S. city gets the most sunshine?

A Houston

B Seattle

C El Paso

D Buffalo, NY

793 What is the Texas A&M motto?

A "Once an Aggie, Always an Aggie"

B "Friendship"

C "To hell with TU"

D "Moooooo"

794 The Permian Basin Petroleum Museum and Hall of Fame is located where?

A Big Spring

B Midland

C Fort Worth

D Permian High School in Odessa

795 Identify the PRCA.

A Public Relations Copywriters Association

B Parents Relating to Children Anonymous

C Professional Rodeo Cowboy Association

D Pornography Research Clearinghouse Administration

796 What San Antonio native took an extra long walk on June 3, 1965?

A Mickey Holden (A West Texas cattleguard ate his car)
B Edward White II (in outer space)
C David Clark (in search of the Dave Clark Five)
D Raul Estrada (walked to Mexico City and back)

797 Who played John Travolta's rival for Debra Winger in "Urban Cowboy"?

A The governor of Nebraska
B Scott Glenn
C Tim Strunk
D Bragg Smith

798 Where did actor Tommy Lee Jones attend high school?

A O.D. Wyatt in Fort Worth
B Cooper High in Abilene
C St. Mark's in Dallas
D King High in Corpus Christi

799 What former Dallas Cowboy lineman wrote a novel about pro football called "On Any Given Sunday"?

A Peter Gent
B Pat Toomay
C Jerry Tubbs
D Jethro Pugh

800 Who was Davy Crockett on television?

A Fess Parker
B Phineas J. Whoopie

C John Wayne
D Chuck Connors

On what university campus in this state can one fine over 40,000 chrysanthemums?
A UT - El Paso
B Rice
C Texas Tech
D Texas Women's University

There is a statue of a 19-foot shrimp in ________.
A The LBJ Library in Austin
B La Grange
C Odessa
D Aransas Pass

Crown Suites are found where?
A The Stephen F. Austin Hotel in Austin
B Texas Stadium in Irving
C Dumas
D In most Midland skyscrapers

Who is Texas' legendary oilfield firefighter?
A Red Adair
B Red Buttons
C R.L. Adair
D Tom Manning

Where did Abilene native Jack Mildren star in college as one of the all-time great wishbone quarterbacks?

A UT - Austin
B Oklahoma
C North Texas State
D Wayland Baptist

 Where did Jayne Mansfield go to high school?
A Corpus Christi King
B Wichita Falls Rider
C Houston Memorial
D Highland Park

 What was the name of Buddy Holly's band?
A The Comets
B The Twilights
C The Crickets
D The Hollies

 What Houston sportswriter coined the term, "Phi Slamma Jamma," referring to the Houston Cougar basketball team?
A Thomas Bonk
B Tom Kennedy
C Kenny Hand
D Scott Kelm

809 What Cowboy lineman illegally caught Roger Staubach's last NFL pass?
A Randy White
B Herb Scott
C Ralph Neely
D Jim Cooper

810 In 1920, who lost to SMU, 70-0, and to Texas, 110-0, in football?

A Texas A&M Aggies
B Rice Owls
C Oklahoma A&M Cowboys
D Daniel Baker Hillbillies

811 Where is the musical, "Texas," staged each year?

A Tower Theater, Houston
B Albany, Texas
C Palo Duro Canyon
D Aboard the Battleship *Texas*

812 Rusk, Texas, has the longest ______ in Texas (546 feet).

A Football field
B Footbridge
C Speed trap
D Field goal record (with the wind)

813 What famous outlaw frequented Tascosa, in the Texas panhandle?

A Billy the Kid
B Son of Sam
C Charles Whitman
D William "Refrigerator" Perry

814 Where is the best-known stagecoach inn in Texas?

A Oakland
B Salado
C Laredo
D Las Colinas

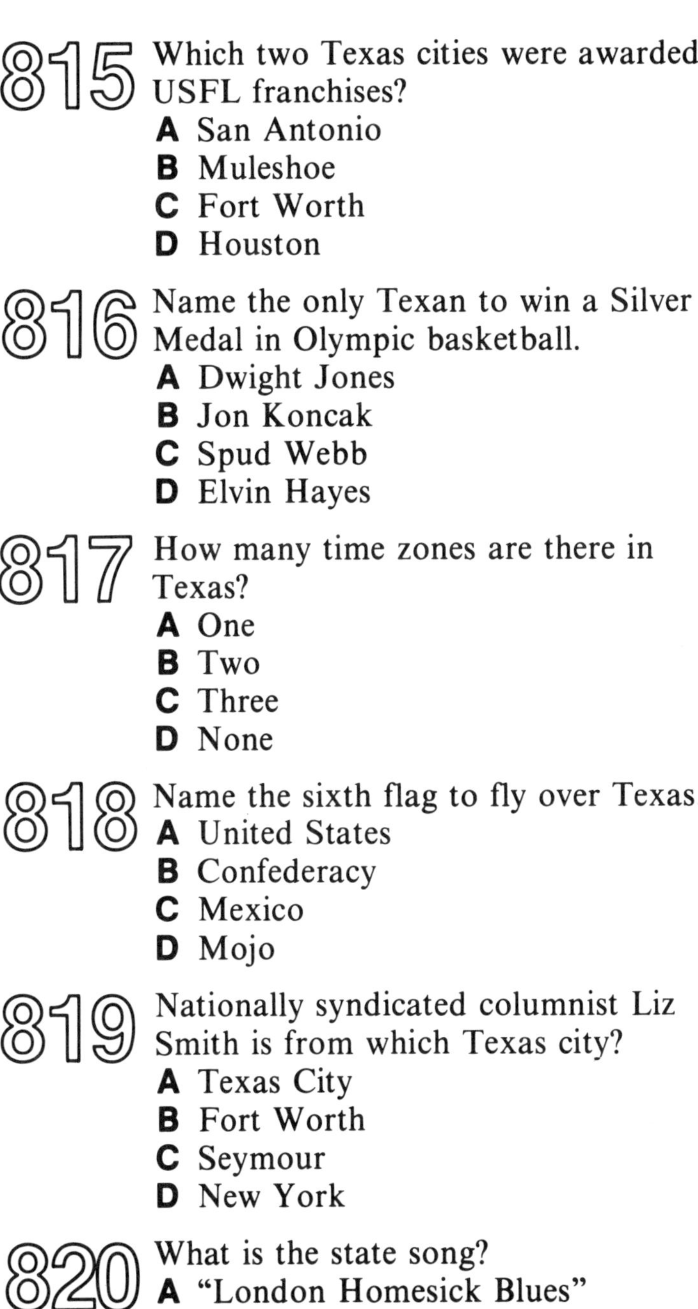

815 Which two Texas cities were awarded USFL franchises?

A San Antonio
B Muleshoe
C Fort Worth
D Houston

816 Name the only Texan to win a Silver Medal in Olympic basketball.

A Dwight Jones
B Jon Koncak
C Spud Webb
D Elvin Hayes

817 How many time zones are there in Texas?

A One
B Two
C Three
D None

818 Name the sixth flag to fly over Texas.

A United States
B Confederacy
C Mexico
D Mojo

819 Nationally syndicated columnist Liz Smith is from which Texas city?

A Texas City
B Fort Worth
C Seymour
D New York

820 What is the state song?

A "London Homesick Blues"

B "The Eyes of Texas"
C "Texas, Our Texas"
D "Texas Fight!"

821 What goat thief got a break from the Texas Ranger who arrested him, which ultimately led to his becoming a country music star?
A Johnny Cash
B Bobby Valentine
C Jay Rosser
D Johnny Rodriguez

822 Name the only U.S. Seaport within railroad switching distance of two countries.
A Port of El Paso
B Rockport
C Port of Brownsville
D Port Worth

In the late 1970's, what Texas airline had a 49¢ fare from Texas to Las Vegas?
A Texas International
B Million Air
C Pacific Southwest
D Gamblers Express

Name all of Rice's 1,000-yard rushers.
A
B
C
D

In 1935, who set the land speed record for an airplane at 352 mph?

A Chuck Yeager
B Howard Hughes
C Wiley Post
D Charlie Hillard

Who was the Alabama player who came off the bench to tackle Rice's Dicky Maegle in the 1954 Cotton Bowl Classic?

A Joe Namath
B Tommy Lewis
C Lee Roy Jordan
D Kenny Stabler

Who played Paul Newman's mistress in "The Life and Times of Judge Roy Bean"?

A Victoria Principal
B Lillie Langtry
C Kathleen Turner
D Tina Turner

What was the color of Santa Anna's silk tent at the Battle of San Jacinto?

A Army green
B Black
C Red
D Polka dots on a baby blue sky

What is a dry hole?

A An oil or gas well which produces no oil or gas
B The act of lining up in front of

Randy White

C The famous solitary confinement cell in Huntsville

D Another name for a double margarita on the rocks

830 What city is called, "Big D"?

A Dumas

B Dalhart

C Dallas

D Duncanville

831 What is the name of the Texas Longhorn cannon?

A Big Bertha

B Bevo

C Old Faithful

D Smokey

832 Which President of the United States enjoyed using his Lincoln Continental to round up cattle?

A Abraham Lincoln

B James Madison

C Lyndon Johnson

D Richard Nixon

833 Joe S. McComb killed over 12,000 what?

A Buffalo

B Comanches

C Houseflies

D Subway muggers

834 The oldest business institution in Texas is _____.

A Electronic Data Systems
B 7-Eleven
C *The Dallas Morning News* (A.H. Belo Corporation)
D Paying high school recruits to play football in the SWC

835 What's the original definition of "maverick"?
A The name of an old television western
B Unbranded cattle
C One of Ford's higher quality products
D What Kiki Vandeweghe is not

836 During the climactic fist-fight in "Giant," what song was playing on the juke box?
A "The Yellow Rose of Texas"
B "Amarillo by Morning"
C "She Got the Goldmine and I Got the Shaft"
D "Dear Darcie"

837 Name the Texas actor who became ET's best friend.
A Tommy Lee Jones
B Henry Thomas
C Jerry Haynes
D Terry Jastrow

838 What Texas town has been listed in the white pages of the Fredericksburg telephone book?

A Crosbyton
B Luckenbach
C Terlingua
D Austin

839 What landed at D/FW Airport on September 20, 1973?
A Braniff stock
B Concorde
C Paratroopers
D Apollo II

840 Jim Bowie and Judge Roy Bean were born in ______.
A Langtry, Texas
B The same year
C Tennessee
D Kentucky

841 Who said, "I'm a powerful SOB, you know that?"
A H.L. Hunt
B Joe Bob Briggs
C Lyndon Johnson
D Santa Anna

842 Where did the Chisholm Trail end?
A The Red River
B Abilene, Kansas
C Canada
D Billy Bob's Texas

843 After gaining more yards than any other rookie in NFL history, what did Earl Campbell buy his mother?

A An autographed Houston Oiler program
B A new home
C The ABC television station in Tyler
D A new dishwasher

844 Thomas Austin Preston, Jr. is better known by his poker name, ______.
A Spoiler #2
B The Son of Austin
C Tommy "White Shoes" Preston
D Amarillo Slim

845 Name the SWC school which is well-known for its ranch management school and the Brite Divinity School.
A Oral Roberts - Austin
B Texas Christian University
C Univesity of Houston
D Baylor

846 When outlaw Sam Bass bought a stranger a drink, what did he use to pay for it?
A The stranger's money
B Gold pieces
C American Express Gold Card
D He never bought a stranger a drink

847 Neal Gay is the legend behind what well-known Texas Rodeo?
A Texas Prison Rodeo
B Kowbell
C Mesquite Championship Rodeo
D Walt Garrison Rodeo

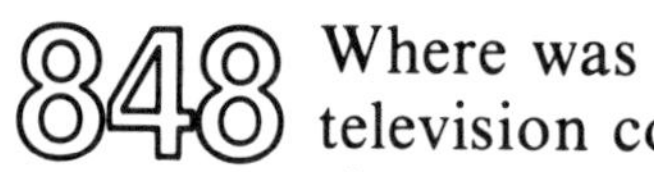

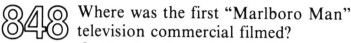

848 Where was the first “Marlboro Man” television commercial filmed?

A The Studios at Las Colinas
B Y.O. Ranch
C King Ranch
D Italy

849 After the Battle of Coleto Creek, in 1836, who surrendered to the Mexicans?

A Colonel James Fannin
B General Sam Houston
C Colonel William Barret Travis
D Colonel Clink

850 Where is Wonder World?

A San Marcos
B Corpus Christi
C South of Big Bend
D North of Houston

851 How many square miles are included in Texas?

A 755
B 34,891
C 267,339
D 24,866,923

852 Who co-wrote and recorded “San Antonio Rose”?

A Delbert McClinton
B Bob Wills
C Waylon Jennings
D Tanya Tucker

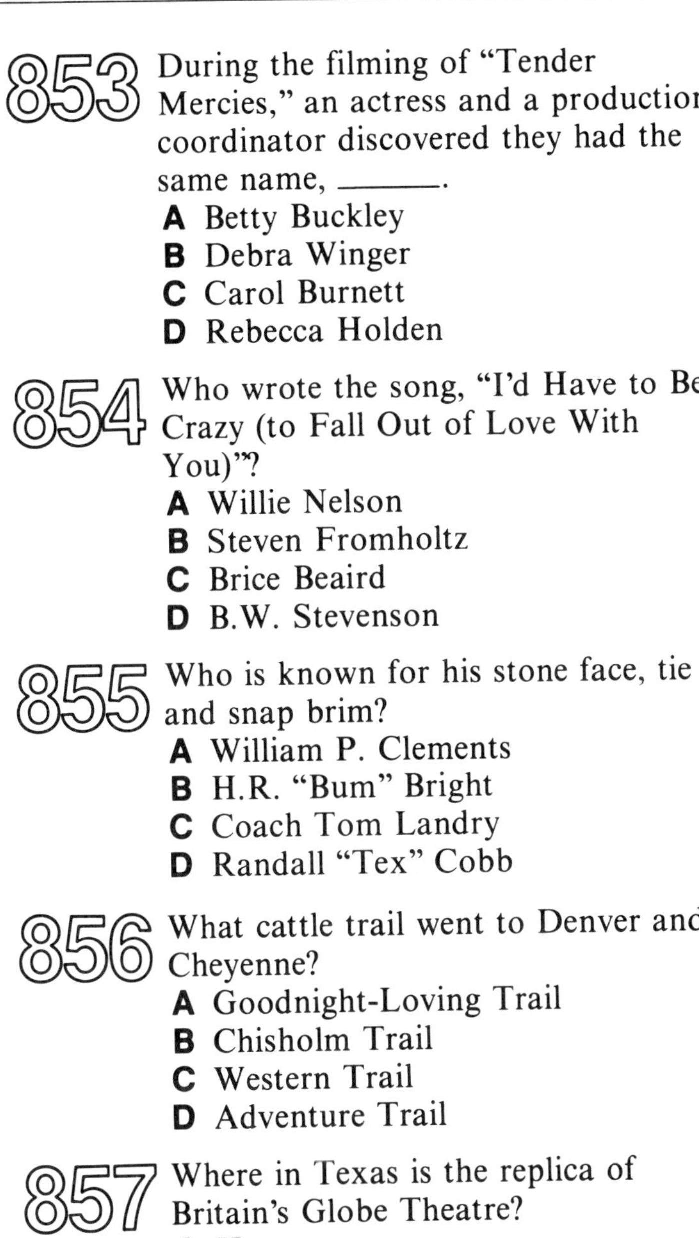

853 During the filming of "Tender Mercies," an actress and a production coordinator discovered they had the same name, ______.

A Betty Buckley
B Debra Winger
C Carol Burnett
D Rebecca Holden

854 Who wrote the song, "I'd Have to Be Crazy (to Fall Out of Love With You)"?

A Willie Nelson
B Steven Fromholtz
C Brice Beaird
D B.W. Stevenson

855 Who is known for his stone face, tie and snap brim?

A William P. Clements
B H.R. "Bum" Bright
C Coach Tom Landry
D Randall "Tex" Cobb

856 What cattle trail went to Denver and Cheyenne?

A Goodnight-Loving Trail
B Chisholm Trail
C Western Trail
D Adventure Trail

857 Where in Texas is the replica of Britain's Globe Theatre?

A Houston
B Austin

C Odessa
D Lufkin

858 What is "Juneteenth", the celebration held each June 19th in Texas?
A Black Texans celebration of the freeing of slaves in Texas
B A large teenage bash held each year in June
C The anniversary of the Battle of Juneteenth
D The celebration of KNOK-FM winning the Dallas ratings war

859 In what year did women first vote in Texas?
A 1836
B 1918
C 1976
D They still are forbidden

860 When accused "Cowboy Mafia ringleader" Rex Cauble went to prison in Big Spring, what mode of transportation did he use?
A His private jet
B Horseback
C His thumb
D Parachute

861 Patillo Higgins and Anthony Lucas drilled what gusher?
A Daisy Bradford #1
B Lucas #1 (Spindletop)

C Jed Clampitt #1
D Wolcott #2

What Dallas sportswriter (and businessman-restaurateur) once turned loose rattlesnakes in the Arlington Stadium Press Box?
A Norm Hitzges
B Steve Pate
C "Honest" Tom Stephenson
D Mike Shropshire

What was the third flag to fly over Texas?
A Mexico
B France
C Spain
D Texas

Name LBJ's personal cook.
A Betty Crocker
B Zephyr Wright
C Lady Bird
D Henrietta Strunk

Which color in the Texas flag, red or white, is on top?
A Red
B White
C Both
D Neither

Brenham is the home of what creamery?
A Borden
B Blue Bell

C Oak Farms
D Foremost

867 Three promoters named Balcom, Morrow and Rhea founded what town?
A San Antonio
B Nacogdoches
C El Paso
D Balmorhea

868 Where is the statue of Mary Martin as Peter Pan?
A Weatherford
B Southfork Ranch
C Mineral Wells
D Never, Never Land

869 R.L. More of Vernon has collected over 10,000 what?
A Gimme caps
B Eggs
C Arrowheads
D Alimony checks

870 Name the oldest county courthouse in Texas.
A Cass County
B Ellis County
C Montgomery County
D Loving County

871 Who is the only man to be head coach of the Rice Owls and The Houston Oilers?
A Bum Phillips
B Jess Neely

C Tom Landry
D Bill Peterson

872 What does the "H" stand for in H. Ross Perot?
A "Handsome"
B Harry
C Henry
D "Hoss"

873 Who was known as "The Raven"?
A Handsome Ross Perot
B Sam Houston
C Johnny Cash
D Quanah Parker

874 Who was Dr. Pepper?
A Mad scientist who invented soft drinks
B There never was anyone named Dr. Pepper
C David Naughton's stage name
D The father of the girlfriend of the drink's inventor

875 In what year did Jim Bowie die?
A 1776
B 1836
C 1845
D 1900

876 Who created "Two-Alarm Chili"?
A Wick Fowler
B Frank X. Tolbert
C David Witts
D Bob LeClerc

877 What southeast Texas university was named for a man who was murdered?
A Baylor
B Rice
C Lamar
D Houston

878 Name the only man to play in the NFL for over 25 years.
A Roger Staubach
B George Blanda
C Don Meredith
D Mike Renfro

879 Who was the female leader of the "Dirty 30" in the Texas Legislature during the 1970's?
A Farrah Fawcett
B Jeanie C. Riley
C Lady Bird Johnson
D Frances Farenthold

880 Who is Ewell D. Walker, Jr.?
A The first Texan shot at the Alamo
B Author of *Lonesome Dove*
C Doak Walker, all time great Texas gridiron star
D The man who turned in Bonnie and Clyde

881 Who built the state Capitol building?
A Spring Valley Construction Company
B Capitol Syndicate of Chicago
C Davy Crockett and a band of

volunteers
D Craig Dooley

882 What is a "Texas Timex"?
A Gold Rolex watch
B Wristwatch with the face in the shape of Texas
C The clock in the wall of a Lear Jet
D A drink made up of tequila, lime and triple sec

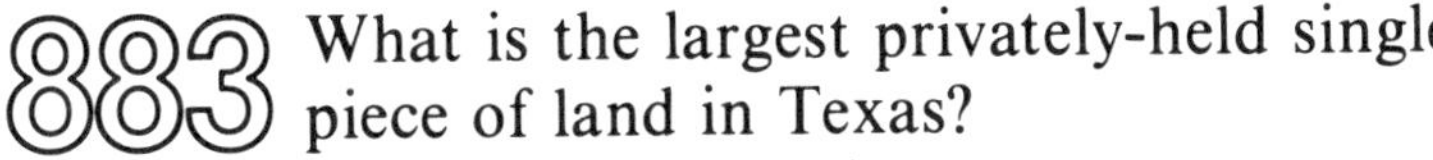

883 What is the largest privately-held single piece of land in Texas?
A The King Ranch
B Big Bend
C Waggoner Ranch
D Bent Tree

884 What was the name of The Crickets drummer Jerry Allison's girlfriend in 1957?
A Annette Funicello
B Peggy Sue
C Becky Nugent
D He didn't have a girlfriend in 1957

885 What is Austin's favorite swimming hole?
A Barton Springs
B Town Lake
C Lakeway
D Chuck Field's backyard

886 Name a Texas Amusement park which is divided into six theme sections.

A Sandy Lake Park
B Six Flags Over Texas
C Wet 'N Wild
D Wonder World

887 Name the leader of the "Texas Jewboys."
A Kinky Friedman
B Bob Wills
C Buck Owens
D Sam the Sham

888 Who is the 52-foot greeter of the State Fair of Texas?
A Bigfoot
B Big Tex
C Ralph Sampson
D Bob Halford

889 What is the most popular rodeo event for kids?
A Bull riding
B Barrel racing
C Calf scramble
D Concession stand

890 Who shared the command of the Alamo with Travis in March, 1836?
A Gen. Bull Simons
B Quanah Parker
C Col. Dickenson
D Jim Bowie

891 What is the loudest bird in Texas?
A Lynda Bird
B Whooping Crane

C Mockingbird
D Screech Owl

Name the first air-conditioned shopping mall in Texas.
A Galleria, Houston
B Dobie, Austin
C Irving Mall, Irving
D Big Town, Mesquite

What Texan was a hobo, dishwasher, gambler, wildcatter and billionaire?
A John Murchison
B H.R. "Bum" Bright
C H.L. Hunt
D Cullen Davis

This Texan has been known for his stormy marriage to Tammy Wynette.
A George Strait
B George Jones
C Gary Morris
D Johnny Lee

What is a "roughneck"?
A Oil field worker
B Linebacker
C People who kick hippies' rear ends
D He who hits dry holes

Name the first store in America to have weekly fashion shows.
A Wal-Mart
B Neiman-Marcus
C 76 Union Truck Stop
D Stephen Craig

897 Name the former woman publisher of *The Houston Post.*

A Babs Greyhosky
B Jean Finley
C Oveta Culp Hobby
D Kim Palmer

What Texas city has one of the five Gutenberg Bibles in America?

A Austin
B Longview
C Carrollton
D Harlingen

The sheriff of what town said, "Them girls are clean, they got regular inspections and didn't allow no rough stuff"?

A Plano
B La Grange
C Sealy
D Texarkana

What are Big Tex's first two words to State Fair of Texas visitors?

A "Stick'em Up!"
B "Ten Coupons"
C "Howdy, Folks"
D "Beat OU!"

901 How many bands are there on an armadillo?

A None
B Nine
C 28
D 29,400

902 In 1950, who was voted by the Associated Press as the greatest female athlete of the half century?

A Nancy Lieberman
B Oveta Culp Hobby
C Mildred "Babe" Didrikson
D Rene Richards

903 There are more Harlem Globetrotters from ______ than there are from Harlem.

A Houston
B Hollywood
C Beaumont
D South Oak Cliff

904 What was the former name of TranStar Airlines?

A Trans Texas Airways
B Fort Worth Air
C Muse Air
D Texas International

905 Who sang the title song in the movie, "Waltz Across Texas"?

A Ernest Tubb
B Waylon Jennings
C Ginger Brown
D Carter King

906 Who directed the movie, "Giant"?

A Ken Harrison
B George Stevens
C George Lucas
D Peter Bogdanovich

907 What is "the Birthplace of Anglo-American Settlement in Texas"?
A San Felipe
B Austin
C Mesquite
D Clear Lake

908 What did Claude Ayers bring to town that was so important that they named the town of Claude after him?
A Women
B The first locomotive
C A bottle opener
D $10,000,000 in gold pieces

909 Which of the following is not a Southwest Conference mascot?
A Horned Frog
B Razorback
C Owl
D Fighting Farmer

910 What Dallas native fought Joe Frazier for the heavyweight boxing title?
A Terry Daniels
B Curtis Cokes
C Harvey Goff
D Ed "Too Tall" Jones

911 What Texas golfing whiz won the 1971 and 1972 Texas Golf Association Men's Amateur Championship?
A Scott Verplank
B Ben Crenshaw
C Tom Kite
D Charlie Adams

912 Who was considered to be Sam Rayburn's protege?

A Lyndon Johnson
B Phil Gramm
C John Connally
D Steve Bartlett

913 Sam Houston and Stephen F. Austin were both born in what state?

A British Columbia
B Kentucky
C Tennessee
D Virginia

914 Who, at the age of 57, was installed as a judge in 1882 by the Texas Rangers?

A Eddie Chiles
B Judge Roy Bean
C Teddy Roosevelt
D Quanah Parker

915 Who was the first Hispanic mayor of a major U.S. city?

A Henry Cisneros of San Antonio
B A. Starke Taylor of Dallas
C Jose Lancaster, Highland Park
D Bob Bolen of Fort Worth

916 What is the "West Point of the South"?

A South West Point, Texas
B Sul Ross University
C Texas A&M
D Southwest Texas State University

917 Who was the Dixie Belle of Dallas?

A Belle Starr

B Bonnie Bee Thompson
C Lottie Deno
D Bubbles Cash

918 He was born Michael Morrison but we knew him as Red Adair and Davy Crockett in the movies. Who was he?
A Red Adair
B Davy Crockett
C William "The Refrigerator" Perry
D John Wayne

919 Name the only SWC football team which has never represented the conference in the Cotton Bowl Classic.
A Rice
B Texas Tech
C TCU
D Arkansas

920 Who owned the Dallas Chaparrals of the ABA?
A Donald Carter
B Brad Corbett
C Robert Folsom
D Wayne Hightower

921 Harvey Martin and Randy White are the only NFL players to both win ______ the same year.
A Their limit of rainbow trout
B The New York state lottery
C Super Bowl MVP Honors
D The respect of Joe Theisman

922 Bored Martyr is a coed's "drinking club" at what university?

A UT-San Antonio
B UT-Tyler
C UT-Austin
D UT-Arlington

923 There is a lifesize statue of Buddy Holly in Lubbock. What is he holding?

A A nice pose
B His breath
C The keys to the city
D His guitar

924 What Houstonian invented the Weedeater?

A Jim Waller
B Donald Bowman
C George Ballas
D Louie Welch

925 Identify "Hoover Hogs."

A WPA workers from Texas who helped build the Hoover Dam
B Arkansas Razorback fans from Hoover, Texas
C Vacuum cleaners used in pig pens
D Armadillos eaten during the Great Depression

926 How many of Red Adair's oilwell firefighters have been killed?

A One
B Only 48

C 259
D None

927 What Baylor basketball coach resigned in 1985 amidst controversy?
A Jim Haller
B Paul Golden
C Meadowlark Lemon
D Elgin Baylor

928 He sang "I've Got a Tiger by the Tail".
A Bulldog Danny Pleches
B Buck Owens
C Stevie Ray Vaughan
D Freddie Fender

929 What 35-foot star weighs 220 tons?
A The morning star above Alpine, Texas
B The star atop the San Jacinto Monument
C There is no star which weighs 220 tons
D The Dallas Cowboy star at the new Cowboy Center

930 In what year was Texas-based Diet Dr Pepper introduced?
A 1965
B 1980
C 1948
D 1962

931 What is "dressing percentage" when used in the context of beef?

A The weight one gains after eating a double cheeseburger
B Percentage of paying beef against a steer's total weight
C How much leather one gets from a cow
D The proper percentage of salad dressing with a steak dinner

932 What U.S. President was instrumental in having Texas annexed into the Union?
A Lyndon Baines Johnson
B U.S. Grant
C James Polk
D Ronald Reagan

933 What Texas Ranch has over 2,500 oil and gas wells?
A The Chicken Ranch
B Waggoner Ranch
C Hackberry Creek Ranch
D King Ranch

934 There is a statue of a what in Fort Stockton?
A Roadrunner
B Chili Champion
C Indian Fighter
D Tourist

935 The huge July, 1969, parade through Houston celebrated what event?
A The Astro's winning the pennant
B The Oilers winning a game

C The first man on the Moon
D Louie Welch coming out of the closet

936 Who was Burt Reynolds' rival for Jill Clayburgh in "Semi-Tough"?
A Nick Nolte
B Don Meredith
C Mac Davis
D Kris Kristofferson

937 Who is credited with inventing the chuck wagon?
A Charles Goodnight
B Buck Owens
C Carroll Shelby
D George Toomer

938 What Texan was the first man to pole vault over 19 feet indoors?
A Don Arnold
B Billy Olson
C Fred Hanson
D Joe "King" Carrasco

939 What is the name of Jay Gould's private railroad car in Jefferson?
A *Atalanta*
B *Jefferson Zephyr*
C *Jay Boy*
D *Excelsior*

940 Where can one find 19,000 gallons of water pumped per minute through five fountains, in a garden setting?

A Wet 'N Wild
B White Water
C Fort Worth Water Gardens
D Astroworld

Name the tallest bird in Texas.
A Whooping Crane
B Roadrunner
C Pelican
D Big Bird

Who sang the song, "Dogs Have Always Been My Friends"?
A Mickey Gilley
B Lyndon Johnson and his dog, Yuki
C Joe and Carolyn Camp
D Kathy Blackwell

Name the Texas street listed in the game "Gay Monopoly."
A Westheimer in Houston
B Guadalupe in Austin
C Midkiff in Midland
D Camp Bowie in Fort Worth

944 What Spanish name did Richard King originally call his King Ranch?
A El Ranchito de Las Colinas
B Santa Gertrudis
C El Rancho de Hatley
D Catarina

945 Before swimmers Mike Heath and Bruce Hayes won gold medals in the same relay in the '84 Olympics, where were they high school teammates?

A Houston Memorial
B Midland High
C Highland Park
D Richardson Pearce

946 Who dreams of Jeanie?
A Eddie Barker
B Larry Hagman
C Patrick Duffy
D Billy Joe McAllister

947 Name the Texas actress who played the original Maggie the Cat on Broadway, although most know her as a Texas matriarch.
A Barbara Bel Geddes
B Ruth Ray Hunt
C Elizabeth Taylor
D Mary Ann Smith

948 Who wrote *Semi-Tough, Dead Solid Perfect* and *Life Its Own Self?*
A Gary Cartwright
B Bud Shrake
C Dan Jenkins
D Jim Atkinson

949 What Port Arthur native desperately wanted a child in "The Big Chill"?
A Glenn Close
B Mary Kay Place
C Lelise Folse
D Jo Beth Williams

950 What Texas-born actress became Paul Simon's mother-in-law?

A Carol Burnett
B Valerie Perrine
C Debbie Reynolds
D Mary Sue Jones

951 What is "Our Gang" star Spanky McFarland's real first name?
A George
B Alfalfa
C Spanky
D Buckwheat

952 What Texas playwright penned *Lu Ann Hampton Laverty Oberlander?*
A Larry L. King
B Preston Jones
C Beth Henley
D Lettie England

953 Who is the yell leader at the Dallas Cowboy games?
A Jim Francis
B Crazy Ray
C Weird Harold
D Randy White

954 Name the first air-conditioned stadium in the world.
A Harris County Domed Stadium
B Texas Stadium
C Kyle Field
D SuperDrum

955 President Johnson had a personal barbeque caterer named ________.

A Ricky Goss
B Randy Goss
C Rocky Goss
D Walter Jetton

956 The Zodiac Room is a legendary Texas eatery located inside what store in Dallas?
A The 7-Eleven at 12th and Edgefield (Hot to Go)
B Starck Club
C Neiman-Marcus (Downtown)
D World Trade Center

957 Gilley's Club in Pasadena had a regular customer named _________ who taught John Travolta how to dance the two-step.
A Gator Conley
B Johnny Lee
C Danny P. Little
D Lynn Ashby

958 What did Texans Tommy Tune, Larry L. King, Carole Hall and Peter Masterson help take to Broadway?
A *Cats*
B *Vanities*
C *The Best Little Whorehouse in Texas*
D *Hurly Burly*

959 What do people kiss in Elmore Park in Shamrock, Texas?
A Each other

B Part of the Blarney Stone
C The bumper of Kent Ware's Chevrolet
D Senior Citizens dressed as lucky shamrocks

What fort near Killeen did Jane Fonda picket during the 1960's?
A Fort Worth
B Fort Hood
C Fort Phantom Hill
D Fort Griffin

What famous Texas oil gusher had a 75-foot geyser shooting out the top of the well?
A Lucas #1 at Spindletop
B Old Faithful
C Daisy Bradford
D Hitzelberger #1

What is Houston lawyer Racehorse Hayne's real first name?
A Racehorse
B Richard
C Cullen
D Harry

What quarterback won 14 of his career victories in the final two minutes of the game?
A James Street
B Don Meredith
C Warren Moon
D Roger Staubach

964 Name two Miss Americas from North Texas.
- **A** Phyllis George
- **B** Stormy Meadows
- **C** Shirley Cothran
- **D** Karen Dower

965 A masked rider on a black horse can usually be found where in Texas?
- **A** Flying through the western sky at dusk
- **B** Robbing a bank in Laredo
- **C** Texas Tech
- **D** Southwestern Cattle Rustlers Association Convention

966 Who makes "Nellie's Jellies"?
- **A** Mrs. John Connally
- **B** Sam "Jalapeno" Lewis
- **C** Nobody
- **D** Mrs. Vernon Baird

967 Who was the owner of the team which lost Super Bowl I?
- **A** Clint Murchison
- **B** Bud Adams
- **C** Lamar Hunt
- **D** H.R. "Bum" Bright

968 What two 1959 All-SWC linemen had sons named after them who went to their dads' alma maters and were named All-SWC in the 1980's?
- **A** Billy Ray Smith (Arkansas)
- **B** Jack Spikes (TCU)

C Bill Glass (Baylor)
D Billy Cannon (Texas A&M)

969 How did Mustang Island get its name?
A An SMU booster gave it to a recruit
B Carroll Shelby tested his Cobra Mustang there
C It was named for the wild mustangs once found there
D Mustang Sally used to cruise the island

970 What is a bitter cold front which hits quickly in North Texas?
A Wind Shear
B Blue Norther
C Panhandle blast
D William Perry up the middle

971 What are the 350-foot cone shaped hills near Quanah which were believed by Comanches to be dwelling places for powerful spirits?
A Vernon Compress Co.'s storage areas
B Medicine Mounds
C Adobe Walls
D Mount Bluewater

972 Captain Charles Schreiner founded what cattle ranch in 1888?
A Y.O. Ranch
B Schreiner Ranch
C Valley Ranch
D Spade and Spur Ranch

973 Name the only poisonous aquatic snake in Texas.

A Diamond-backstroke rattlesnake
B Cottonmouth (water moccasin)
C Water snake
D Grapevine python

974 What Boston Celtic star won the 1986 NBA 3-point shot contest, held in Dallas?

A Kevin McHale
B Larry Bird
C Blake Taylor
D Spud Hitzelberger

975 Where did Texas horses originally come from?

A Billy Jack drove them in from New Mexico
B Mexico
C Southern Oklahoma
D Spain

976 What Texas wildcatter was on the cover of *Time* in 1950?

A J.R. Ewing
B Jett Rink
C Glenn McCarthy
D "Dad" Joiner

977 Why is April 21 celebrated each year in Texas?

A Income tax returns start being sent
B It's the anniversary of the Texas victory at San Jacinto

C April 21 was the day prohibition was ended
D Texas became a state on April 21

978 Where was the first rodeo ever held?
A Pecos
B Colorado City
C Stamford
D Fort Worth

979 What material was *not* used to build the State Capitol?
A Granite
B Wood
C Limestone
D Green argon tubing

980 What is the most widely distributed fish in Texas?
A Catfish
B Tuna
C Swordfish
D Bass

981 Where was the first national bank in Texas?
A Houston
B Dallas
C San Antonio
D Galveston

982 What happened to the Texas coast town of Indianola?
A It went bankrupt
B It was blown away by hurricanes
C It burned down

D It changed its name to Corpus Christi

983 Stamford's Texas Cowboy Reunion is the nation's oldest and biggest open __________.

A Rodeo
B Carnival
C Oldtimer's football game
D Reunion of ex-Dallas Cowboys

984 What piece of legislation was passed in 1913, allowing oilmen to deduct as much as a fourth of their income before paying taxes?

A No pass, no play
B Oil depletion allowance
C Law of 1913
D Self-serve gasoline allowance

985 Identify "the Big Beer from the Littlest Brewery."

A Lone Star
B Falstaff
C Shiner
D Pearl

986 Where was the "Hook 'em Horns" hand sign introduced?

A At the 1955 Texas pep rally before the TCU game
B In Washington D.C. when LBJ became President
C At the Battle of the Alamo
D In Darrell Royal's office when his secretary did it

What Luckenbach legend called himself an “imagineer”?

A Waylon Jennings
B Bubba Hart
C Buddy Holly
D Hondo Crouch

Who was the first woman colonel in the U.S. Army?

A Mrs. Almaron Dickenson
B Miriam “Ma” Ferguson
C Oveta Culp Hobby
D Cindy Kate Briscoe

What is the name of the covered wagon which rolls into Texas from the north each October?

A The Blue Norther
B Sooner Schooner
C 20-mule team Borax
D Silverado

990 There is no such thing as an ex-________.

A Aggie
B Marine
C Con
D Patriot

Sam Bass only robbed trains and what else?

A Banks
B Stagecoaches
C Old men playing dominoes
D Girl Scouts

992 Acquired in 1965, programmed by Salaam Qureishi and used by Mr. Brandt, what is this Optimum Systems unit known as?

A The Southern Baptist Church
B OPEC
C Music Television
D The Dallas Cowboy computer

993 Name two Texas women named Candy who were tried and acquitted in sensational murder trials.

A Candy Barr
B Candy Mossler
C Candy Coker
D Candy Montgomery

994 How did the bluebonnet flower get its name?

A Lady Bird Johnson named it
B It's blue and resembles a pioneer woman's headcovering
C The Republic of Texas held a contest to name it
D They didn't want to call it a bubonic flower

995 Who blazed the Goodnight-Loving Trail?

A Charles Goodnight
B Mike Hatley
C Oliver Loving
D Davy Crockett

996 What "Father of Austin Country Music" got the first beer license in Travis County following prohibition?
A Jerry Jeff Walker
B Willie Nelson
C Darrell Royal
D Kenneth Threadgill

997 Who is the world-famous actor who, as a child, learned how to swim at the Baker Hotel in Mineral Wells, while his mom was a singer there?
A Robby Benson
B Gary Busey
C Larry Hagman
D Kris Kristofferson

998 "Let's Padre!" means:
A "Let us pray"
B "Have you met my father?"
C "Let's party at Padre Isle!"
D (Unmentionable)

999 Gene Stallings left the Dallas Cowboys in February, 1986, to become the head coach at ________.
A Texas A&M
B St. Louis
C New Orleans
D Harlem Globetrotters

1000 Who caught James Street's 4th down pass to help UT beat Arkansas in the 1969 national championship "Big Shootout"?

A Jim Bertleson
B Steve Worster
C Cotton Speyer
D Randy Peschel

1 D Spud Webb
2 B "Why Baby Why"
3 D Will Rogers
4 A Fort Worth
5 C Rio Vista
6 B San Antonio
7 C Alan Bean
8 B Eddie Chiles
9 A Bing Crosby
10 D Robert Benton
11 C Astrodome
12 B *The Sunset Limited*
13 B Waco
14 B San Felipe
15 C 254
16 D Fort Worth
17 A Sulphur Springs
18 C The Cotton Bowl
19 A Anti-union sentiments
20 D SMU
21 C Bob Wills
22 A Athens, Texas
23 D Pecan
24 B Roger Staubach
25 B White shoes
26 C Gas lights
27 C Ferguson Jenkins
28 A Texas A&I
29 B Collie
30 D Linda Gray
31 C Rip Torn
32 B Roger Miller
33 D Larry McMurtry
34 B Patsy Cline
35 B Sandhill State Park at Monahans
36 C Pecos
37 A Astrodome
38 B El Paso
39 A Bloodrock
40 A *Friday Night Heroes*
41 D Odessa, Texas
42 C Petroleum
43 B Baylor
44 A Big Bend National Park
45 C Republic of Texas
46 C Three weeks
47 B April 21
48 D Austin
49 A St. Anthony's in San Antonio
50 C UT-Austin's Memorial Stadium
51 C Mike Renfro
52 B "Terms of Endearment"
D and "Urban Cowboy"
53 A Dennis Hopper
54 B Armadillo
55 C Tom Landry
56 B Washington-on-the-Brazos
57 A Eugene, the undertaker

58 B Barn Dance
59 A Parkland
60 A North Texas State University
61 A 18 minutes
62 A Buddy Holly
63 C Fort Worth
64 D Second tallest peak in Texas
65 C Chief Peta Nocona
66 A Houston
67 D Jerry Tubbs
68 A Greg Ryan of SMU
69 B "The Girl Can't Help It"
70 D In a bank in the middle of Beverly Hills...
71 A Lake Texoma
72 B Padre Island
73 D Earl Campbell
74 C Lois Chiles
75 B Hobby Airport
76 C To attend Billy Graham's rally
77 C Seceed from the Union
78 D Sign the Texas Declaration of Independence
79 C At least 21
80 D Ruby's attorney Melvin Belli
81 C Jay Coburn
82 A Stanley Marcus
83 A Robert Duvall
84 D Austin
85 C Sweetwater
86 A Mount Vernon
87 D Willie Nelson
88 C Steve Kanaly
89 D Thomas Thompson
90 B The Lost Gonzo Band
91 A John Wayne
92 C Elvin Hayes
93 C Doak Walker
94 A Archie Bell and the Drells
95 D Canadian River
96 D Pearl
97 A Topaz
98 B Meatloaf
99 D Tex Watson
100 B Rice Stadium
101 D Jack Heifner
102 C "Gone to Texas"
103 C Texas Schoolbook Depository
104 A New Braunfels
105 B "State Fair"
106 A Beulah
107 B Hottest day
108 D Stephen F. Austin
109 C Bob Hayes

0 A Bud Adams of Houston,
D Lamar Hunt of Dallas
1 A "Written on the Wind"
2 C ? and the Mysterians
3 D Oil was discovered
4 A Box 13, Jim Wells County
5 C Real grass wouldn't grow
6 B An ax
7 A Santanta (or White Bear)
8 C Billie Sol Estes
9 A Speaker of the House
20 C Betty Buckley
21 D Howard Hughes
22 C Carroll Shelby
23 B Rick Nelson
24 A El Paso
25 C At the LBJ Ranch
26 A Kenny Stabler
27 D Texas (The Erwin Center)
28 B Red McCombes of San Antonio
29 C Cliff Hagen
30 B "Urban Cowboy"
31 A Las Colinas
32 C Patrick Duffy
33 B Fritos
134 D Brownsville to Perryton
135 A Active Catholic parish
136 C At *The Dallas Morning News*
137 A Fredericksburg
138 B A grapefruit
139 C Secretary of Treasury
140 A Chili
141 B The Battleship *Texas*
142 D Michael Nesmith
143 D Kris Kristofferson
144 A Blues
145 B Austin
146 B Trans Texas Airlines
147 C American Buffalo
148 B Ramos Gin Fizz
149 B Delta Tau Delta
150 D Buddy Holly
151 B William Barret Travis
152 B Lone Star Cafe, NYC
153 B Tidelands mineral rights
154 A Snyder
155 A Danny Faulkner
156 C Greenville, Texas
157 D Beer
158 A Sakowitz
159 C The Klebergs
160 A Jody Payne
161 B Jerry Argovitz
162 D Fredericksburg

163 B Gene Goss, The Tradin' Hoss
164 D Southern Methodist
165 A John Lang Sinclair
166 B Tommy Lewis of Alabama
167 C Karen Master
168 B Horton Foote
169 D Lubbock
170 C Singer Boz Scaggs
171 C Rice
172 B Navigation Street
173 C Wild Turkey
174 B Seashore
175 A Oceanography
176 B Muse Air
177 C Longview
178 A Polish
179 C Museum
180 B Houston Rockets
181 A Waco
182 B Debbie Reynolds
183 D Willie Nelson
184 C The Port of Houston
185 B Two survivors
186 D "I Threw My Mother-in-law in the River"
187 C 27
188 B Martin Jurrow
189 D London, England
190 B Lake Travis
191 A Kareem Olajuwon
192 C Fort Hood
193 B Beaumont
194 D Chuck Latourette
195 B Texas Tech Red Raiders
196 A Dusty Hill
197 C "Remember the Alamo!"
198 B Spaniards living in the new world
199 A 7¼
200 C *The Spruce Goose*
201 C Canada
202 B Dallas
203 A The University of Texas at Austin
204 B San Felipe
205 B The University of Texas at Austin
206 D Mean Joe Greene
207 A Lyndon Johnson
208 B Mexican-American War
209 C The Dallas Cowboy Cheerleaders
210 D Anglo
211 C Mia's
212 B Meatloaf
213 C Mac Davis
214 A W. Lee "Pappy" O'Daniel
215 C Charley Pride
216 C Littlefield

7 A Houston (Goodyear)
8 B Hyatt Corporation
9 B Missouri, Kansas and Texas
0 A B C D All of them
1 D Big Bend National Park
2 A Fort Worth
3 A Santa Gertrudis
4 C Highland Park Shopping Village
5 D Bick
6 A Ernest Tubb
7 B Mike Schmidt
8 C Texas Stadium
9 B Austin
0 B Roger Staubach
1 A Sheriff Jim Flournoy
2 C Asleep at the Wheel
3 B Baton twirling
4 A The Globe Theatre
5 A Kim Tomes
6 C Roy Orbison
7 D Teddy Roosevelt
8 B "Hud"
9 D Bill Bradley
0 A Texas A&M
1 B Odessa
2 C Norm Bulaich
3 C The Prince of Wales
4 A WBAP, Fort Worth
5 D Deep yellow
6 D Lamar Hunt

247 D Midland
248 C Eddie Phillips
249 B The Academy Awards' Oscar
250 B Odessa
251 C Barbara Jordan
252 B Goodyear blimp
253 B Beauford Jester
254 B John Heisman
255 A Don Meredith and C Danny White
256 D Waco
257 B Colorado
258 B David G. Burnet
259 A J.D. Tippit
260 C Gilley's
261 C President of SCRA
262 A Charlie Dunn
263 B A.J. Foyt
264 B Miriam "Ma" Ferguson
265 D The Spanish
266 C Johnny Ringgold
267 A Jett Rink
268 D Houston
269 B Bonnie Parker
270 B Mickey Mantle
271 D Don Gay
272 C Wichita Falls
273 A Tyler
274 B "Bulldog"
275 D Charles Hardin Holley

276 B Last Indian fight in Texas
277 B Stephen F. Austin
278 A Trinity
279 B Gulf coast line
280 A His own
281 C Drive-in
282 D Peter Gent
283 C Texas became the second largest state
284 B Texarkana
285 B Battle of Laredo
286 B Gordon Wood
287 C Odessa Permian
288 D "She Got The Gold Mine . . ."
289 A "Electric Horseman"
290 B "Lone Star"
291 B Janis Joplin
292 D Sam Rayburn
293 B 1968 (HemisFair)
294 A NASA
295 C Coors
296 A Billy Sims
297 B O.A. "Bum" Phillips
298 B Frank Beard
299 D "Hud"
300 B Mockingbird
301 B Dalhart
302 C Dallas Tornado
303 A Beaumont
304 D Round Rock
305 D Roy Orbison
306 A Harlingen
307 A Brazos
308 A Panna Maria
309 A King Ranch
310 C Baylor
311 D David Bowie
312 D Dallas-Fort Worth Turnpike
313 B Buck Owens
314 C "The Last Picture Show"
315 C Vera Jane Peers
316 A Lone Star
317 C Friends
318 A Mike Ditka,
C Raymond Berry
319 C Sarah Dodson
320 C State Fair official greeter
321 B Francisco Vazquez Coronado
322 A Jack Nicholson in "Terms of Endearment"
323 B Alan Shepard
324 A Marfa
325 A Gene Street,
B Phil Cobb
326 D Presidio
327 C White Flash
328 A Lyndon Johnson,
D Dwight Eisenhower
329 D Clyde Barrow

0 B San Antonio's 250th
1 D 1866
2 B Gene Upshaw
3 A Diron Talbert
4 A Janie Fricke
5 A Brazos
6 D The United States
7 B Price Daniel, Jr.
8 C LaSalle's French settlement
9 B Kathy Whitmire
0 C Carroll Shelby
1 C Mexico
2 C Larry L. King
3 D Gale Storm
4 B Houston
5 A Luckenbach
6 A Texas leaguer
7 B Lurch
8 D Frito's
9 A Stanley Marsh 3
0 B Frijole
1 A The Von Erichs
2 B Impact
3 C First Baptist, Dallas
4 D Davey O'Brien
5 D Ron Meyer
6 C "Lefty"
7 A "Benji"
8 D Texas Atomic Energy Research Foundation
9 C Alaska
0 B Kilgore

361 A La Grange
362 B Apache Indians
363 B SMU
364 D The late, great Joe Miller
365 B Menger Hotel in San Antonio
366 D In the back of the head
367 A Trini Lopez
368 B Cuero, Texas
369 B Richard Widmark
370 B Airplane crash
371 C "Viva Max!"
372 A University of Houston - UCLA
373 C King Gill
374 A Charles Speyer
375 B Chilimpiad
376 D 1885
377 A Luci Baines,
C Lynda Bird
378 C Houston
379 A Midland
380 C Ruby's sister, Ava Grant
381 C Saracen
382 B Mr. Telephone
383 B Arcadia, Louisiana
384 A Harold Taft
385 B XIT
386 A Tyler Petroleum Club
387 B Alpine

388 C Winston Hill
389 C Lloyd Ruby
390 C Pat Garrett
391 A Pearl
392 B Gordon McLendon
393 C Bob Hope
394 B "Friendship"
395 B A professional wrestler
396 C "Houston. Tranquility Base here. The *Eagle* has landed.
397 B 1718
398 B Ben Hogan
399 A The Diablos
400 C Beaumont
401 B Judge Roy Bean
402 C Lavaca Bay
403 A To operate a steamboat
404 D North Texas State
405 B Don Nottebart (1963)
406 A Archer City
407 A Baylor (Pat Neff Hall)
408 A San Jacinto Day,
C Texas Independence Day
409 C A railroad
410 B "Hud"
411 D "Dallas"
412 B Waco
413 C Masterminding the "Cowboy Mafia"
414 A Cuellars of Dallas
415 C San Antonio
416 C Two
417 A Race car driver
418 B Robert Benton
419 D Chili
420 B Steve Worster
421 B Barbed wire
422 A Pasadena, Texas
423 C Arlington Heights
424 D Bevo
425 C Rio Grande
426 D James Street
427 A "Walkin' the Floor Over You"
428 B Mexican food galo
429 D *Texas*
430 B Galveston
431 B Clint Longley
432 A Lorenzo de Zavala
433 A Palo Duro State Park
434 C Ima Smith
435 D Seventh Day Adventists
436 B Hurricane
437 C Kinky Friedman
438 C "He Never Killed a Man Who Did No Deserve Killing"
439 B Twenty-eighth

0 A Lubbock
1 B Indian pictographs
2 D Texas A&M
3 A George Strait
4 D Guadalupe
5 C San Jacinto Monument
6 B Laredo
7 C Jack Johnson
8 D The Dallas Rangers
9 D Jimmy Demaret
0 D Lubbock
1 B At the San Jacinto Battlefield
2 A Candy Barr
3 B Highland Park Shopping Village
4 B Buttermilk
5 B Fourth of July
6 A Guy Clark
7 B Jimmy Dean
8 B Elmer Wayne Henley
9 C He was killed in a car wreck before the movie was released
0 D John Tower
1 C A bottle thrown at the referee
2 C Hassie
3 B Pool and deck areas
4 A Joan Robinson Hill
5 C Houston
6 C *The Fort Worth Press*

467 C Fowler and Smith
468 B Tommy Tune
469 C Cartoonist
470 D C.M. "Dad" Joiner
471 B Lamar Muse
472 C Part of a 20,000 year old skull
473 C Marvin Zindler
474 D Fort Wolters
475 B Dolph Briscoe
476 D Houston
477 B Brownsville
478 B Jefferson
479 A Texas State Railway
480 A 773 miles
481 C Bob Wills
482 D Larry Hagman
483 B Juarez
484 D Possum Kingdom
485 A Dallas
486 D Floydada
487 A Ted Williams
488 A Brick
489 B Austin
490 B Santa Gertrudis
491 A Jim Reeves,
C Tex Ritter
492 C "Waltz Across Texas"
493 A The Port of Houston
494 D San Jacinto
495 C Lillie Langtry

496 D He wrote the document
497 C Lyndon Johnson
498 C Palmwood
499 A Muleshoe pitching
500 C Courage, purity and loyalty
501 A Charlie Brooks, Jr.
502 C Bubba Jennings, Tech
503 D Spain
504 D Nacogdoches
505 A Jan Korkamus
506 B Reata
507 B Robert Strauss
C John White
508 A Dr. Red Duke
509 C Texas Declaration of Independence was signed
510 B Lubbock
511 D The Cisco Kid
512 A Hollywood (Landmark Hotel)
513 C Liquid Paper
514 B Houston Cougar basketball team
515 B Bobby Morrow
516 A Inez Perez
517 A Sarah T. Hughes
518 D Gary Hammond, SMU
519 B Col. Tom Lubbock

520 A First Monday
521 A Debra Winger
B Shirley MacLaine
522 C Buddy Holly
523 C Gary Cartwright
524 A Longview
525 C 1986
526 C Texas Taxi
527 B Albert Thomas
528 B Gov. Pat Neff's mother
529 B Rangerettes
530 A Texas
B Texas
C Texas
D Texas
531 C Picosa
532 D *The Eagle*
533 D Richard Nixon
534 D None
535 B "Ike"
536 C He was hanged in 1877
537 B Rugby player
538 D Jean Lafitte
539 A Woodward Mauri Ritter
540 A Houston vs Dallas (AFL)
541 D Ken Hall (Sugarla
542 B Billy Bob's Texas
543 B Garland
544 B Weslaco

5 D Marfa
6 B Texas Tech Red Raiders
7 D Danny Davis of Houston
8 B Michael Murphey
9 C Gene Autry
0 A Icky Twerp
1 C On the third floor
2 A Roy Orbison
3 B Dan Moody
4 C The Nueces
5 D Resigned
6 A Sunday
7 C New Mexico
8 B Edmund J. Davis
9 D Cancer
0 C Red River
1 B The Southland Corporation
2 C Dwight Eisenhower
3 A Mexico's defeat of France in 1862
4 A Sammy Baugh
5 D Brad Corbett
6 A Linda Lovelace
7 B Dan Jenkins
8 B Lubbock
9 D Willie Nelson
70 A Jim Nabors
71 A 1880
72 C Kareem Olajuwon
73 C Sammy

574 A Kern Tips
575 B Debra Winger
576 B Seals & Crofts
577 A Robert Redford
578 C UCLA
579 B Tony Fritsch
580 A Gregory Gym
581 B Coors
582 B Debbie Reynolds
583 A Lavender
584 C Mockingbird
585 D Houston San Jacinto
586 D Dallas
587 A Pine
588 C Ranger Peak
589 A The Eyes of Texas
590 B Governor John Connally
591 B I-45
592 A A seven-foot strawberry
593 B The Capitol Building in Austin
594 D Michael Levy
595 B Roadrunner
596 A White Deer
597 B United States
C Texas
598 B El Chico
599 A Austin
600 A Dallas
601 B The LBJ Ranch
602 A Brownwood

603 C Darrell Browder
604 C Cliff Harris
605 D Brownsville
606 D One
607 A Southwest Airlines
608 C Chaps
609 B "Viva Max!"
610 C Jerry Levias
611 C Santa Rita #1
612 D Pecos
613 B Baines
614 A Green Valley
615 A 1972
616 D Atheist
617 C Willie Nelson
618 B St. Mark's, Dallas
619 C Shirley Temple
620 A During the hot season
621 B France
622 C Johnson Lake
623 C Dr. J.E. Pearce
624 B Fort Sam Houston
625 C Lyndon Johnson
626 C They were all named Jose
627 A Geoff Huston
628 C Thousands of grasshoppers
629 B Moses Malone
630 A Roy Rogers
631 A Johnny Nash
632 C Gen. Robert E. Lee

633 C Coral Snake
634 B Cactus
635 D Texas Women's University
636 B Missouri and Paci
637 A Houston
638 B Crosbyton
639 A Grand Prairie
640 A McDonald Observatory
641 D Larry Gatlin
642 B Craig Morton
643 B Billy Shoemaker
644 B Astronaut
645 A Fort Worth
646 D Johnny Lee
647 A Cybill Shepherd
648 B Robby Benson
649 C Trinity
650 D Oklahoma
651 B Kike Vandeweghe
652 A Farrah Fawcett
653 B Post
654 C The Baytown Tunn
655 B Texas Capitol site
656 A Waco
657 A Baylor University
658 C Bill Moyers
659 B Salt
660 C Tilapia
661 B The Alamo
662 A Bob Wills

663 C His basket beat the Cougars
664 A Frank Lloyd Wright
665 B Sculptor
666 D River Oaks
667 B Phil Burleson
668 A Spoetzl
669 B Frito-Lay
670 C Texas
671 D Morgan Fairchild
672 A Dean Martin
673 B Floyd Cramer
674 A Tommy Lee Jones
675 C Sherman, Texas
676 B "Galveston"
677 D Lyndon Johnson
678 B U of Virginia didn't have one
679 C 31 years
680 C Tomato
681 B San Antonio
682 A Brazos
683 B Edd Hargett
684 D Norm Sonju
685 C Charles Paddock
686 C DeWitt Weaver
687 A Interstate Theaters
688 B Four
689 A Paula Prentiss
690 C North Street
691 C One of his own men
692 D Escalators
693 B Astrodome, Houston
694 A Aboard *Air Force One* at Dallas
695 B Bob Wills' steel guitarist
696 A John B. Stetson
697 C Weatherford
698 B Paisano
699 D Wiley Post
700 A Gerald Hines
701 D Memorial Park
702 C Stan Farr
703 C 1976
704 B Martin Jurrow
705 B Richardson
706 C Cadillac Ranch
707 C Diamonds cut in the shape of Texas
708 D Over 200
709 B Elizabeth Forsythe Hailey
710 A Lone Star Beer
711 C Edgefield and 12th in Dallas
712 A John Nance Garner of Uvalde
713 C Gary Busey
714 B Lenel Geter
715 C Billy Dixon
716 A William "Bigfoot" Wallace
717 A Braniff International
718 D Gene Autry
719 B Ima

720 A David Witts
C Carroll Shelby
721 D Waylon Jennings
722 A Henry Wade
723 C Ecomet Burley, Texas Tech
724 A Lee Westbrook
725 C The Two-Step
726 D His jeans
727 B Ponder
728 B LBJ Library
729 D Cow Servants
730 A Bob Beamon
731 A "Vanities"
732 D He was hanged
733 C Pittsburgh
734 C Jimmy Seals
D Dash Crofts
735 B Barbara Mandrell
736 C San Antonio
737 B "Bull S____!"
738 B World War I
739 B England
740 D Dolph Briscoe
741 B The Carousel
742 C Tech mascot used to be a Matador
743 D "The eyes of Texas are upon you"
744 D None
745 C Treaty of Guadalupe Hidalgo
746 A Bluebonnet
747 D His divorce papers
748 C E.H.R. Greene
749 B Gail Borden
750 C Coronado
751 B Jane Long
752 A J.P. Richardson
753 B Claire Chennault
754 D Abilene
755 D New Orleans
756 A Plano
757 C San Antonio
758 C Kermit
759 B Dallas
760 A Ganders
761 C Keith Bobo
762 A Butch Johnson
763 B Freddie Fender
764 D Houston
765 A New York Giants
766 B Conway Twitty
767 C Carolyn Jones
768 B Peter Bogdanovich
769 D Watermelon
770 C Lyndon Johnson
771 A Marfa
772 C Grass
773 A They struck oil
774 B Him and Her
775 A Cisco
776 C Dave Smith
777 A H.L. Hunt
778 B Las Colinas in Irvi
779 C Lee

80 D Fort Worth
81 A Texas Panhandle
82 D Harris County Jail
83 C Roger Staubach
84 A Aquarena Springs
85 C Wurstfest in New Braunfels
86 B Horse rustling
87 B Roy Orbison
88 D Hondo
89 D Baylor
90 C AR
91 C She was Miss America
92 C El Paso
93 A "Once an Aggie, Always an Aggie"
94 B Midland
95 C Professional Rodeo Cowboy Association
96 B Edward White II
97 B Scott Glenn
98 C St. Mark's in Dallas
99 B Pat Toomay
00 A Fess Parker
01 C Texas Tech
02 D Aransas Pass
03 B Texas Stadium
04 A Red Adair
05 B Oklahoma
06 D Highland Park
07 C The Crickets
08 A Thomas Bonk
809 B Herb Scott
810 D Daniel Baker Hillbillies
811 C Palo Duro Canyon
812 B Footbridge
813 A Billy the Kid
814 B Salado
815 A San Anotnio
D Houston
816 A Dwight Jones
817 B Two
818 B Confederacy
819 B Fort Worth
820 C "Texas, Our Texas"
821 D Johnny Rodriguez
822 C Port of Brownsville
823 A Texas International
824 A There are none
B
C
D
825 B Howard Hughes
826 B Tommy Lewis
827 A Victoria Principal
828 C Red
829 A Non-producing oil or gas well
830 C Dallas
831 D Smokey
832 C Lyndon Johnson
833 A Buffalo
834 C *The Dallas Morning News*

835 B Unbranded cattle
836 A "The Yellow Rose of Texas"
837 B Henry Thomas
838 B Luckenbach
839 B Concorde
840 D Kentucky
841 C Lyndon Johnson
842 B Abilene, Kansas
843 B A new home
844 D Amarillo Slim
845 B Texas Christian University
846 B Gold pieces
847 C Mesquite Championship Rodeo
848 B Y.O. Ranch
849 A Colonel James Fannin
850 A San Marcos
851 C 267,339
852 B Bob Wills
853 A Betty Buckley
854 B Steven Fromholtz
855 C Coach Tom Landry
856 A Goodnight-Loving Trail
857 C Odessa
858 A Celebration of freeing of slaves
859 B 1918
860 A His private jet
861 B Lucas #1 (Spindletop)
862 C "Honest" Tom Stephenson
863 A Mexico
864 B Zephyr Wright
865 B White
866 B Blue Bell
867 D Balmorhea
868 A Weatherford
869 B Eggs
870 A Cass County
871 D Bill Peterson
872 C Henry
873 B Sam Houston
874 D Father of the girlfriend of the inventor
875 B 1836
876 A Wick Fowler
877 B Rice
878 B George Blanda
879 D Frances Farenthold
880 C Doak Walker
881 B Capitol Syndicate of Chicago
882 A Gold Rolex watch
883 C Waggoner Ranch
884 B Peggy Sue
885 A Barton Springs
886 B Six Flags Over Texa
887 A Kinky Friedman
888 B Big Tex
889 C Calf scramble

90 D Jim Bowie
91 B Whooping Crane
92 D Big Town, Mesquite
93 C H.L. Hunt
94 B George Jones
95 A Oil field worker
96 B Neiman-Marcus
97 C Oveta Culp Hobby
98 A Austin
99 B LaGrange
00 C "Howdy, Folks"
01 B Nine
02 C Mildred "Babe" Didrikson
03 A Houston
04 C Muse Air
05 B Waylon Jennings
06 B George Stevens
07 A San Felipe
08 B The first locomotive
09 D Fighting Farmer
10 A Terry Daniels
11 B Ben Crenshaw
12 A Lyndon Johnson
13 D Virginia
14 B Judge Roy Bean
15 A Henry Cisneros
16 C Texas A&M
17 A Belle Starr
18 D John Wayne
19 B Texas Tech
20 C Robert Folsom
21 C Super Bowl MVP Honors
922 C UT-Austin
923 D His guitar
924 C George Ballas
925 D Depression armadillos
926 D None
927 A Jim Haller
928 B Buck Owens
929 B San Jacinto monument star
930 D 1962
931 B Paying beef against a steer's total weight
932 C James Polk
933 D King Ranch
934 A Roadrunner
935 C The first man on the moon
936 D Kris Kristofferson
937 A Charles Goodnight
938 B Billy Olson
939 A *Atalanta*
940 C Fort Worth Water Gardens
941 A Whooping Crane
942 B Lyndon Johnson and Yuki
943 A Westheimer in Houston
944 B Santa Gertrudis
945 C Highland Park
946 B Larry Hagman

947 A Barbara Bel Geddes
948 C Dan Jenkins
949 B Mary Kay Place
950 C Debbie Reynolds
951 A George
952 B Preston Jones
953 B Crazy Ray
954 A Harris Co. Domed Stadium
955 D Walter Jetton
956 C Neiman-Marcus
957 A Gator Conley
958 C *Best Little Whorehouse*
959 B Part of the Blarney Stone
960 B Fort Hood
961 A Lucas #1 at Spindletop
962 B Richard
963 D Roger Staubach
964 A Phyllis George
C Shirley Cothran
965 C Texas Tech
966 A Mrs. John Connally
967 C Lamar Hunt
968 A Billy Ray Smith
C Bill Glass
969 C Wild Mustangs
970 B Blue Norther
971 B Medicine Mounds
972 A Y.O. Ranch
973 B Cottonmouth
974 B Larry Bird
975 D Spain
976 C Glenn McCarthy
977 B San Jacinto Day
978 A Pecos
979 D Green argon tubin
980 A Catfish
981 D Galveston
982 B Blown away by hurricanes
983 A Rodeo
984 B Oil depletion allowance
985 C Shiner
986 A 1955 Texas pep ra
987 D Hondo Crouch
988 C Oveta Culp Hobb
989 B Sooner Schooner
990 A Aggie
991 B Stagecoaches
992 D Cowboy computer
993 B Candy Mossler
D Candy Montgome
994 B It's blue and looks like a bonnet
995 A Charles Goodnigh
C Oliver Loving
996 D Kenneth Threadgi
997 C Larry Hagman
998 C "Let's Party at Pa Isle!"
999 B St. Louis
1000 D Randy Peschel